Shar

by Lynn Crawford

For:
BILL CRAWFORD
JOHN CORBIN
DETROIT BIKRAM
LINDA CRAWFORD
SANDRA SCOPPETTONE

GRATEFUL ACKNOWLEDGMENTS

"George" originally appeared as
"Compiling Information,
My Way by George Shankus"
In the online literary series *No News Today,*
Robert Lopez editor, May 2011

"Tap Tap Tap"
originally appeared as "Meg,"
in *The Unbearables Big Book of Sex,*
Ron Kolm, Carol Wierzbicki, Jim Feast, Steve Dalachinsky,
Yuko Ottomo, and Shalom Nauman, editors
Autonomedia/Unbearable Books, New York, New York, 2011

An earlier version of *Shankus & Kitto: A Saga* was published as
Shankus & Kitto by Black Square Editions, New York, 2016

Cover image: *Flip Book, Page 2, 2011*
Mixed media by Matt Zacharias
48 individual pieces (12x12 inches each)
Courtesy Simone DeSousa Gallery, Detroit, Michigan

ISBN: 978-0-692-76085-7

Published by DittoDitto, 1548 Trumbull Ave, Detroit, MI 48216
http://www.dittoditto.org

CONTENTS

Ily   6

George   20

Meg   29

George   44

Meg *(with contributions from Emily)*   49

Emily   66

George   75

Meg *(with contributions from Emily)*   82

Emily and Meg   105

Emily   115

Ily   125

Ily Shankus

(birth surname: McGee)

People/people who need people/are the luckiest people...
Jule Styne and Bob Merrill

Some things seem impossible until they happen to you (acne, a long kiss, heartbreak).

I do not consider the comfort and constrictions of my close-knit family, our small town, and the sense of purpose and direction they provide until I leave.

Senior year, high school, overseas culinary program. The acceptance, with full scholarship, is a Big Deal for me and our community. I am seventeen.

I travel alone, arrive before classes start. My mom planned to join me those first weeks, but we decide I should go alone. Gain independence. Meet people. Visit museums, markets, a pool. Taste street food, spring for a nice meal, maybe even get invited to a private home.

I fly alone and tear up as the plane takes off. Embarrassed, I spend the flight pretending to sleep until the meal (which includes a fantastic wedge of cheese) comes. I navigate the airport and bus lines to my new address. I meet the concierge, who leads me up several sets of stairs and tells me not to drink water from the tap. She lets me into my assigned attic room, gives me a key, and leaves me sitting on my new room's scuffed floor. I am slammed with a complex set of emotions. Unprepared: Can I live in this place a whole year and how am I supposed to hydrate? Excited: I am going to learn how to cook. Really cook. From experts.

By the way – I have a small victory at the airport. After I retrieve my luggage and find and board the correct bus, the bus driver asks me for the fare, but I don't have it. Why? Lost backpack. I retrace my steps, find it hanging on the toilet stall peg, and believe this is a good signal. Then, on the new bus, I meet a guy my age (super handsome) who doesn't look American but turns out to be. His name is Dino, and he is here to study food, too. More on him later.

The first few days I wander around this new city, totally wishing Mom was here but so happy she is not. I will miss home. Miss cooking on Sundays after church and before choir. Miss gardening, baseball, tending our bees. Miss how my laundry smells. Miss sleeping, studying, playing music in my bedroom with its flowered paper, the dresser and shelves Dad built. My books. I recite them here when lonely: *Good Night Moon,*

Invisible Man, Nancy Drew, Fear of Flying, Their Eyes Were Watching God, Bleak House, Suzuki Beane, If Beale St Could Talk, All of a Kind Family, Harriet the Spy, The Godfather, Wuthering Heights, Mrs. Piggle Wiggle, Anna Karenina.

I miss my books and also miss going to Friday night football, fitting in, having friends, being considered a part of something.

Yet I sense potential for personal and professional expansion. Realize how little I know. This city values beauty in ways I don't understand. My clothes feel wrong, and food portions are modestly sized and gorgeously presented. I develop mixed feelings about things I never thought of before: Dad's toothpicks and belly laugh. Mom dressing in Dad's button-up shirts, not just at home but out shopping. People who speak only English and understand only our town and county but not the wider world. The fact we are so serious about church and our iced drinks.

These thoughts make me feel guilty, traitorous.

But I need them.

I just do not have anywhere to put them.

Plus, I spend complicated time with Dino and have no one to talk to about that.

Community and conversation never seemed like a Big Deal, but in their absence, they are. At home, we chat constantly, but only *during* things (like driving, folding, gardening, cooking, mowing, canning) when we are likely to be interrupted, unlikely to make eye contact.

Here, people engage, or seem to. They walk arm-in-arm or sit, heads bent together, smoking, talking, sipping from small cups and glasses. Also they read and write *in public*. Wear v-necks, scarves, slim fitting pants and skirts. I want to be with them. Actually, to be honest – and this might sound creepy – I want to *be* them. I don't know where to go with that urge. The sensory intake puffs up, puffs me up, and I feel as if I've swallowed something porous, stubborn, indigestible.

I meet a few people, some connected to my program, others at the swimming pool.

The Americans are friendly. Frankly, over friendly. I do not travel all this way to hang with them, track down where to find a big breakfast or bread that works with peanut butter, discuss TV shows we cannot get here or sports teams. Complain about warm soda. I might never love it here, but I want to learn. I hope to meet locals, chefs, cultivate patrons. But, so far, people who live here do not seem to want to hang with me. Probably because of reasons mentioned above but also due to my general inexperience with and ignorance of politics, history, fashion, conversation. And my bad accent. I do not blame them. I mean, they have not yet tasted my food, and that is what I have most to offer.

Dino is in a completely separate category. I am just not ready to go there now.

I guess things might change once the structure of school starts.

My letters home are affirming, purpose driven, not expressive. (*I am safe, miss u! Learning a lot! Can you send my blue scarf?*)

I try to express some things in the journal my high school gives me as a going-away present. A senior class group picture is on the cover, and "Bon Voyage" is written across the top. I fill the first few pages with poorly structured sentences, lists, exclamation points, stars, diagrams, but it comes out awful. That voice I put down on paper captures nothing of what I go through, of what I mean.

I do not have a specific face, ear, or sensibility to direct my thoughts to. It is the first time in my life. Never realized I always had a built-in audience. Family, neighbors, teachers, friends. People mildly interested in me, at least. Maybe not a burning interest, but enough to notice if I am sick or dirty or get a haircut or make the honor roll. To eat – and provide friendly feedback on – my Halloween pumpkin stew, my Christmas kuchen, my state-fair tongue tacos, vegan "meatballs," scrambled eggs with leeks, cream cheese potato chips. ("Your tongue is yummy," they might say. "Perhaps a bit over pickled," I've heard. "Chips have an excellent crisp.")

Away from that, I feel excited yet uneasy. Reckless.

Then, one day, at a table, on the sidewalk, I hear a conversation.

I am in cut offs (not the cool form-fitting hot pants women here wear with wedged heels but sloppy ones that hit mid thigh), an untucked t-shirt, a headband, and threadbare moccasins. I sit at an outdoor place, drinking juice, sketching foods I miss (beef, corn, milk) in my Bon-Voyage notebook. A woman – blue dress, black stockings, sunglasses with thin red rims – sits down at a table next to me. I grow alert and not just because she is beautiful and exotic. (She is.) I sense something brewing. Straight off, I know I am safe to observe. No way will she register me as a person of interest. I think of the Miss Marple movies Mom and I watch and how the detective solves multiple cases through smarts and not standing out. That is me today. An invisible force. I am certain this woman would enjoy my cooking, maybe even like me in some situations, but not today.

A man (sport coat, Bermudas, leather binder) joins her. They converse in low tones in English. Some energy transfers from them to me. I turn the page on the beef, corn, milk and start on a new recipe: chicken, lavender, figs. Those two are talking about something meaningful. I feel it, and I am now doing something meaningful, too. Quark, syrup, rose water, pistachios. Onion fennel pie. Napoleons.

Their words are low, inaudible at first. I hear individual words – "organ," "droop" – nothing complete. The word "organ" hits home. It is my bond with the American, Dino, on the bus. We both travel here to study ways to prepare and cook traditional offal.

Soon things with my neighbors heat up. I sit straight, hear a full sentence: "And then something happens to me, just after turning forty, that I never anticipated: I fall out of love with my vagina."

She continues. She soon realizes she is not really out of love with that organ but that our culture is. It falls stone cold out of love with mature vaginas. And culture does the same with the aged penis. Young genitalia, tight, springy, and smooth, are valued not for their beauty – beauty is make-believe anyway – but for their purpose. Youthful sexual organs are at the height of their reproductive powers. Thematically this is pure Marquis de Sade, the repressive link between sexual acts and procreation. This is something her dear late friend Angela Carter wrote and spoke about eloquently.

The name Marquis de Sade, another homer. My Great Grandmother (may she rest in peace) spoke so fondly of the Marquis, about how his writings greatly championed The Cause.

This solves a huge problem for me because Great Grandma is exactly the person to filter all my new experiences through, to direct my thoughts to.

My first thought directed her way: Is the sex-organ aging process the same for traditional males and females as it is for Bobby, my big brother who is transgender? Would she know about that? Probably yes and, if no, she would know who to ask.

My table neighbors sip tea that smells herbal, maybe citrus, though I might be mixing the smell with my own juice drink.

Great Grandma would be interested in how I think and feel here, without judging. I ease into my seat, feel a lightness enter my body, and listen to the woman say that when she falls out of love with her vagina and grows critical of her vulva, she is alarmed and ashamed but is motivated to address the problem. She crouches above a mirror every morning for a month and examines texture. Memorizes each crevice, fold, protuberance. Gets reacquainted and then falls back in love. She decides on a course of action: creative reconstruction. Not Surgical. Think: mind game. To Re-Form/Re-Think/Re-Make how she views – we view – aging/aged vaginas and penises.

Now, several years later, she has developed a fragrance for full-grown adults, ready to launch, that hints (not directly, of course) at seasoned beauty that is fresh, fulfilling, exotic. The blend for women includes berry, cedar, ginger.

Then she speaks of the aged penis. How she never fell out of love with that. How it tastes, she believes, better than a young one. It radiates confidence and has nothing to prove or brag about.

Her fragrance for "him": bourbon, milk, and a whiff of nutmeg.

Certain cultural standards, she knows, value the anus over a vagina or penis. She does not judge, she wants to be clear. This is not good, not bad. It just is. Everyone has an anus. It is the great equalizer. But she is interested in difference, hence the focus on the (once but no longer) reproductive sexual organs.

As my neighbor in the blue dress talks, I cannot help but wonder how her vagina likes being inside those black hose. The day is warm. Perhaps it is cooped up, hankering for air. But maybe her stockings are held up with a garter and are not pantyhose. I think of my mom and her toned dancer's legs always bare in this kind of weather.

The man, who I guess is a journalist or a potential financial backer, asks about marketing.

She tells him her photo-shoot idea.

A fellow with good seasoned biceps and a white t-shirt and sunglasses is on a sailboat. His hand has to be in the picture somehow. A good watch on his wrist, and maybe he's cradling a beer can or rigging a sail.

A woman in comfortable but not casual dress (maybe a close-fitting white dress) and big earrings, kitten heels, lots of eyelashes is poolside.

She says people equate water with things free, stimulating, gutsy. That is why she would not want either model inside a library or office or kitchen. Definitely not a bedroom. Too blatant. Future campaign settings: skyscraper's rooftop, seaside wine bar, air balloon.

How can I be here all this time, of course, and not look toward Great Grandma as my community? I love her so much. She lived through war, poverty, illness, losing a child and husband, working as a spy. Dealing with some very bad guys and contributing to their arrests, imprisonment, and in some cases executions. She always listened to me talk and even seemed intrigued. For sure, I can tell her about what goes on here, even about Dino.

Great Grandma. I will not only "talk" to her. I will write her letters. Maybe she will even read them. I believe in heaven, and I believe she is there. I do not know if people in heaven listen to people on earth. I do not know if they have that level of interest. I believe they love us. I just question their interest level.

It is sweet to finally feel a sense of personal structure and organization. I learn my Great Grandma's history from my grandparents and parents and, when I am older, some journals, letters, and the authorized biography, which was made into a very good movie. The more I learn, the more I wish I did not waste our time together blabbing about me: a boy, my bike, our beehives. My relish, omelets, and honey cakes. I regret not asking her more about her.

But now, now I can tell her about how nothing prepares me, a Midwestern American, for the glamour of this city. I know about its cuisine but not its distinction. Great Grandma knows all about elegant European cities, having been born in one that flourished, got destroyed, and was then rebuilt. But I have no idea. My first sense of this place (I can say this only to her because it sounds so ignorant, so judgmental) is that it's overly decorated. Then I realize I can tell her all I want but will not get her feedback. So I have to imagine it. Imagine her response. Already, I see my opinion on things aesthetic is misguided. Yet I am confident Great Grandma understands (would understand?) the context of my blooper.

My hometown has nothing higher than one- and two-story buildings. Most things there are one of three colors: green (leaves, lawn, awnings), black (roads, streetlamps), and brown (treetrunks, dirt, roofs). Buildings are for use, not inspiration. We live, worship, post, learn, transact, and eat in them. They are not meant to pulse, radiate, or house treasures.

That is why being here, in this region of "decor" (walks, trees, parks, river, bridges, benches) is such a contrast. The structures (government offices, museums, apartments, shops) are majestic and useful. The combination made me nervous, even suspicious, at first, but now I see it as something I might be able to incorporate into my cooking. Possibly.

Anyway, "Description before judgment," Dad says.

The outside of my apartment: reinforced concrete with ceramic cladding and double doors with leaded glass.

Inside: mirrors, parquet floor, winding staircase. Worn, good quality carpet. Men wearing slip-on shoes and vests. Children with backpacks. Women in heels and fitted sweaters. Small dogs. Nice old musty (but not bad like old books) smell. Windows on every landing. No screens. Heat but no air conditioning.

My room is in the attic.

It is advertised as a garret. The word sounds romantic, but there is *nothing* tender about a stuffy space with a sink, floor mattress, and single window.

The toilet (shared) is two floors down.

There is no shower or bath. I use the sink to brush my teeth, wash my face, rinse off. But maybe it is good there is no shower because that spurs me to join a swimming pool that has showers. It plays an important part in my year.

This detailing is getting boring, and if it is boring to me, it might also be boring to Great Grandma. Sorry. I wish there would be a hurricane or thunderstorm or a flock of birds flying through my window. Or a riot.

Or that I find a set of steps from my garret down a back stairway to an indoor swimming pool with colorful tiles, showers, and saunas. Maybe with a bar serving lemonade, tea, almonds, and absinthe poured from a luminous green bottle.

My garret is dispiriting until Dino starts to visit. Nothing matters once we grip one another on the mattress, with bad bedding, or on the floor. He comes and goes through the window because you need a key to enter the building and I live several floors up. The window entrance sounds romantic but, honestly, is not because he has to jump from the neighboring roof top (it's filthy, he says) and land on the sill one flight below me and then scale up to my window, a journey that worries me every time. If it rains, he comes in drenched, and there is really no good way for him to dry off. I have a few hand cloths and rags but no bath towel since I shower only at the pool. And when it is hot, he works up such a sweat. He is dirty – his hands, shoes, shirt. Sometimes he is in a bad mood because of the looks he gets from my neighbors who see him climb past their window. But once we start, we do not care about greasy hair, soot, gossip, bird droppings, sopping clothes, body odors. Until he leaves, I never feel dirty or sad or lonely. Then I do. And it is bad.

Yet being in that hurt space is what gets me out to the pool. I have to walk fifteen blocks. Long blocks, not like the small squares in our town. Without that empty feeling, I probably would not exercise and bathe regularly, and that teaches me the value of routine, discipline, structure.

Also – and this might seem random – I keep thinking of the word "valiant." Along with "heroine," "courage," and "stamina." Anyway, this city seems valiant, too. I'm not valiant, not yet anyway, and neither are my parents. They are first-rate, not valiant. "Diligent" is another word for them. "Responsible" is another. But valiance, I'm guessing, requires braving specific dangerous situations with grace before you triumph.

I feel cheerful about having Great Grandma back in my orbit, but I feel a little guilty, knowing what she lived through. Do I sound spoiled? I know that I am. Maybe it is irritating for her to hear one of her offspring detail things so insignificant. But maybe she would be relieved that I am safe, that my concerns are menial. And maybe having her on my radar will help me accept me (homesick, culinarily ambitious, uninterested in style, children), prioritize success, not things troubling me. I learn to be productive, reach my potential (be the best chef I can be).

I have to find that balance between engaging with the world and keeping myself apart from it so that my ideas are fresh and my drive strong. Otherwise, I will get gobbled up. And this might be the start of what some people call my being chilly or driven or anti-social or at least not the kind of friend you can lean on. You can depend on me, yes, but lean, no.

George Shankus

Everything is kept inside/So take a chance and step outside.
Ian Kevin Curtis, Peter Hook, Stephen Paul David Morris
and Bernard Sumner

My brother, Dino, and I are born an hour apart on the Upper
West Side of our city. (I am older.) Our family (three kids, two
parents, visiting relatives) is not rich, but we live in a four-
bedroom apartment with a big kitchen, a dining room, and three
bathrooms. Nearby, there are markets stocked with good quality
food, clothes, and most things we need (hardware, toiletries).
Everyone says this now, and they have been saying it for years:
Our city has become impossible for regular people to afford.

Families who recently move into our neighborhood are
wealthy in ways we are not and never will be. They are the kind
of wealthy where they employ full-time cooks, housekeepers,
personal trainers, and drivers. They are also, for the most part,
agreeable people invested in their community, city, economy,

and political system. Those kinds of investments are attractive when things go your way, when you can choose where to work and live, whom to marry, what to eat and wear. When you can offer your children detailed, varied experiences, and continue to have them yourself.

The family that now lives next-door to my parents is that kind of wealthy. They invite us to Easter dinner and serve rice with almonds, baby lamb chops, green beans. Their children – two sets of twins – have a vanilla-and-coconut frosted bunny-cake for dessert. We adults get scoops of sorbet doused in Prosecco.

The rich people in this city have a jaw-dropping amount of money. Not like my cousins who live in the Midwest and enjoy a specific form of affluence. They have a fraction of the income our new neighbors have, but they own a massive house, on a semi-circular street of other big homes, with large back yards, in the middle of nowhere, though you constantly hear the near-by highway. The closest supermarket is a ten-minute drive away and is in a strip mall. The stores there are for eyeglasses, hardware, clothing, sports equipment, cutlery. There is an Ethiopian restaurant.

Some families are musical. Others are athletic, artistic, spiritual, stylish. My family is a family of eaters, and our favorite food group is meat. Not one member of the Shankus family can get away from it: chicken, veal, kidneys, sweetbreads, pork, liver, turkey, giblets, beef – but especially lamb. We go to church, all Greeks we know do, but when Dad talks about religion, he says,

"Our God is the rice, vegetables, and meat that we are blessed to work with each day."

Our parents, born in Greece, meet as children on the boat over where their folks became friendly. Mom's family is from Sparta. She has blond hair, blue eyes, and fair skin. Dad's family is from the Peloponnesians. They have dark hair and complexions. I take after mom in the coloring department. My sister, Georgia, has dad's dark complexion. (We call her "Ja.") Dino is in between. Our parents are hard workers. They have to be. But they are also content. In fact, not one of us three kids is as happy in love or in work as they are. They run a small restaurant, "SHANKUS," around the block from the apartment. It has a neon sign in the shape of a lamb with our family name in red below it. The animal is white and outlined in turquoise blue.

"That is the color of the ocean in Greece, the exact damn color," says Dad.

"Your father needs glasses and cannot admit it," Mom whispers behind his back. She helps manage the restaurant. She works, even when we are little. Because we have so many relatives, Mom has an easy time getting someone to watch us. Now, with parents today, this does not seem so easy, to get family members, or any free help, to watch your children. We hear this all of the time from Ja, who tends to play victim. I love my sister and relate this as fact, not judgment.

"Ok, Mom worked, but she had all of those relatives to care for us. Who do I have to help me? Who, George and Dino, who?"

Ja has three children. She is always talking to us about why she does not work. Not that we ask. Not that we care. But she feels this need to tell us constantly about why she cannot work. She lives in a large house – almost as big as our Midwest relatives' – in a small town a short train ride from the City.

When Ja wants something, she strategizes. Getting the attention of her now husband and former boss, Nick, is an example. He owns the real estate office she works in after college. When his marriage dissolves, she makes a beeline. "I want him," she tells us one Sunday morning. Within six months, they are engaged. Now they have the children, the house, and Nick still runs his realty office. But Ja complains that he comes home every day and sleeps and won't trim his nose hair, which is alarmingly long, or even let her do it.

At a family gathering two Sundays ago, their youngest daughter, Cathy, stuffs food up her nose and starts screaming. I get her on the counter and tweeze out bits of rice and ground meat. Ja cries and shouts about herself: "I am a terrible mother. I will never be the mother our mom was. Never ever." Mom dozes in her rocking chair next to Nick, lightly snoring on the couch. Dad is out with Dino for a walk.

So Ja is disappointed. I guess I am, too, which might explain why I devote my life to outcome, specifically asset accumulation. People want to be rich for different reasons. My motivation is simple: Wealth equals protection, and money equals safety. If I never need what I acquire, family members and friends might. Knowing I can take care of them is a comfort. I own several buildings in the city and live in one of them, not far from my parents' place.

I start every day moving, gotta work up that sweat. My routine: jump rope, push-ups, jump rope, sit-ups, jump rope, dumbbells (arm curls, flies, squats), jump rope, then a specific series of stretches. It lasts, with stretching, forty-five minutes.

My first stop out of the house is my brother Dino's restaurant, "SHANKUS TWO." Like SHANKUS, SHANKUS TWO has a neon sign, but it is of two lambs. Their dark little noses touch one another. Their thin white legs stand upon a bright patch of green. SHANKUS TWO is eighty blocks downtown from SHANKUS. It serves what my brother calls "modern" versions of the SHANKUS menu. What Dino means by modern is healthy.

When Dino and his wife, Meg, first move downtown (into one of my buildings) there are American diners, Hungarian soup shops, French cafes, a German beer hall – but not a place that you could call modern (healthy). SHANKUS TWO is ground level. They live above with their young daughter, Althea.

SHANKUS TWO is wildly successful financially, but my brother is exasperated.

His neighborhood, filled with young adults, some starting families, boasts Zen meditation and massage centers, studios offering yoga, Pilates, Nia, and organic clothing and body care stores. This focus on physical and spiritual well-being determines the kinds of food SHANKUS TWO serves. The neighborhood clientele is vegetarian or vegan and demands as much organic as possible.

The organic is not a problem.

SHANKUS TWO makes a small fortune off their organic smoothies, their white and green teas. They regularly sell out of squash soup, beet salads, kale stir-fry, and red-lentil patties. They win awards for rice pudding, baklava, honey yogurt. This success does not make Dino happy because for Dino there is no cooking without meat, and here is where he runs into his SHANKUS TWO problems. Meat is precisely what he loves to cook and precisely what he cannot sell and therefore does not cook. Diners don't purchase it. This depresses him. Profoundly. One day, he runs twelve miles, and the next he retreats behind a wall of silence.

This morning, I visit. My brother is fit, with slightly thinning hair and even white teeth. He hugs me before he complains, "George, this neighborhood is killing me."

He slides a mug of shade-grown Mexican coffee my way. On the counter there are jugs of half-and-half and soy creamer. Pots of agave and honey, a bowl of raw sugar. About a year ago, I used the soy creamer accidentally and liked it. This morning, I add it to my mug.

Late last night, I left my brother, who was gloomy and rolling dolmades with nuts and rice. This morning, his mood has not improved.

"It used to be, George, I could slip a little lamb in – just a little tiny morsel – and pass it off as mushrooms or dark tofu, but you can't get away with that these days. Taste my barley soup. Pure crap."

He hands me a spoon. I taste. It is not bad, but even one ladle of meat broth would improve it. I tell him so.

"I know. And I will sell this shit out, I tell you. Look at them," he continues, nodding toward a crowded table of women and men, eating sweet-potato olive hash. (Another top seller.) Carefully groomed painted toes peep out of the women's hemp and nylon mesh sandals. The men, full heads of hair, sit erect, one in half lotus. "Not a meat eater in the fucking group. For a while, I got some of them to go with me on the High-Quality-Meats-from-Animals-that-Lived-High-Quality-Lives campaign, but they faced peer pressure, you know. They all do yoga, and some of their teachers toe a hard dietary line." He nods toward a diner at the end of the counter, chewing a millet-date muffin. "Would you look at her jaw muscles."

"Dino," I say, "Stop feeling sorry for yourself."

Silence from my brother.

"Look how well you did with that cookbook *D&I: Offal.*"

"George, what the fuck does that mean if I cannot serve offal?"

"Dino, you have a good life – a good family, a profitable business. If you don't like the way you have to run it here, in this neighborhood, fucking move."

He nods. "Good idea, George. Good. Fucking brilliant. And do what, exactly, with my wife and daughter?"

I do not understand why this is such a problem – this idea of moving – but do not have the patience or time to delve into it this morning. One thing I know about my brother is that he has problems balancing what he wants to do with what others want him to do, especially his wife, Meg, and our father. Dino makes solid decisions, but because he is not very good at explaining them, he comes off secretive, even sneaky.

For example, just after high school, Dino wants to study cooking in France. Our father is furious.

"France? You think goddamn France can teach you more than I can, than Greece can? What, you think France is better than Greece?"

Dino does not push his point. Dad thinks he wins. We all think so. Until one warm late summer morning, we find a note on the kitchen table, capital print letters:

WILL SEND YOU MY ADDRESS IN PARIS. LOVE, DINO.

Mom sits down and sobs. Dad bangs his fist on the wall and then stands silent. His back heaves up, down. After a few minutes, Mom dries her eyes, puts her hand on Dad's shoulder, and says, "It will be good for him and us. Trust me. Drink your coffee. Let's go to work."

He nods.

Ja and I look out the window as they stroll, hand in hand, down the street to SHANKUS. Ja sits down and plays our organ, and I strum my guitar. We have lots to take in.

Later, Mom tells us she acted quickly to bring Dad back, or he would tip over the edge. We understand, increasingly, this is her role, or one of them: keep dad earthbound. Even I, the person closest to Dino, did not know of his Paris plans. Later, when we talk, he explains he did not tell me because, if he did, I might tell Dad or at least feel obliged to tell him, and he did not want to put me in that bad position. This is typical Dino. He does something that seems underhanded but is not. His aim is true.

Meg Kitto

Must I paint you a picture/ about the way that I feel?
Billy Bragg

You can choose who you love but not who loves you. It takes me a long, grueling time to grasp this. I wish it had not.

I tell myself and anyone who will listen that I am wrecked when Dino leaves, especially because he leaves me for that chef Ily, who is upstate and who he met in cooking school years ago in Paris and then together wrote that big seller *D&I: Offal*. But, if I am honest – and it does not feel great being this kind of honest – I am not shocked.

Being torn up about something is not always the same thing as being taken by surprise.

It makes it easier to be upset when they are the same or when you pretend that they are.

I had the right to be torn up but not surprised.

I see it coming and so do others. And this makes it even worse. The "He never really seemed that into you" or "You two never seemed right together" comments. Not "He loved you so much he could not handle it" or "He is incapable of loving anyone but himself."

The fact is that Dino's exit is probably the right thing.

Initially, I process what happens in ways all about me: I am flawed. I am and always have been. We all are. It is the human condition. But my flaws are extensive. Ily's are few, perhaps barely existent, so he leaves me (bad) for Ily (good – or at least better).

The thinking escalates. He leaves me (boring) for her (captivating). He leaves me (easy) for her (complex). He leaves me (drab) for her (hot). He leaves me (a stuffed, furry teddy bear) for her (a silky, smooth minx).

I understand this is just my making up stories, but don't stories help you hold onto hope? Don't they help generate motion when dreams are dashed, help divert attention from a life that is dull and crappy?

What is the difference between making up stories and being delusional?

That question, which is unanswerable, helps me move on. Objectively, how deeply flawed can I be? I have friends, a daughter, a good relationship with my family and with Dino's. I like my job – a manager at my aunt's contemporary clothing store,

Simply Separate. I am carefully groomed. I wear flattering but not flashy clothes. I have moisturized skin, clean conditioned hair (long, naturally blond). I get waxed (brows, upper lip, legs, and a regular bikini-plus). I am in okay shape. No, I don't spin or kick box or take Pilates or yoga classes, like most women in my neighborhood. But I hula hoop, belly dance, and stretch most mornings at home, so I am not super fit but not flabby or un-toned. I love to eat, just let me say that. No one would call me thin. I have large hips, which help during childbirth. Althea just slips out. No snipping, tearing, or incision for me. I drink pineapple juice every day and daub tea tree oil with a q-tip once a week around my vagina, so I always smell and taste good. I know it works because I check. Plus, and this is petty and perhaps mean spirited to share: George tells me one night that Dino, while drunk tells him I taste better than Ily. George, telling me this one night when I am broken down in tears. George is and always has been protective of me. Perhaps he is over sharing, but, boy, does that potent piece of a story comfort me through some dark times.

My shortcomings appear way before Dino.

But I learn early flaws do not equal failure.

I am not a child who functions well outside of our home. Not on the playground or ice rink, not in girl scouts, piano lessons, summer camp, school. So no one in my family is surprised when my parents are called in for a teacher conference. Mom takes me to school. (Dad, as usual, is working.) She enters the classroom with two teachers who gesture to a plastic stack chair in the hallway and ask me to wait. I sit. The building walls are thick, but the room's door has a thin window that makes it possible for me to hear.

"Your daughter is simple," one of the teachers says.

"Also uncooperative," the other says.

"She is – do not take this wrong, Mrs. Kitto – not equipped for us here."

"She is not engaged."

"Are you expelling her?" asks Mom.

"No," the one teacher says.

Silence.

"Yet, you might consider sending her somewhere else," the other says.

This is my memory of the conversation.

It may or may not have exactly happened this way.

I am upset.

The teachers are partly right but mostly wrong. I might appear disconnected but definitely do not just sit at my desk like a slug. I am busy, involved. Maybe I am with my own thoughts. Some people call them daydreams, and they come from things I see and hear at school. I am not like the bored and lazy kids who mouth off, zone out, get high. That is not my situation. True, I have weak test scores, a messy desk, not a ton of friends. But I take in material and even produce – just not grammatical sentences, science reports, and math sheets showing all work neatly.

My problem with school is I hear sounds when my teachers speak, even words I sometimes understand individually. But everything blurs together and makes no sense. I see a safety pin at the bottom of a skirt, a pearl jammed in an ear, hear the instruction – lesson six – all at once. The words and the person saying them are like a gravel pit, glassy lake, or stormy sky. They are things to take in and sense, not to comprehend and recite back. I cannot string together the pieces of information transmitted in school, cannot re-state them. Too many other things lobby for attention: lights, posters, hair, saliva, movements, smells. Clark, who is cute; Bob, who is not. The floor tiles, the loudspeaker announcements, the visitors, the window views. Notes written in ink on my desk. ("Meg & Clark," "H-U-N-G-R-Y," "mathsucks.") The teachers' skirts, blouses, full-skirted dresses. Their (sometimes) bunchy nylons. Their feet jammed inside oxfords, kitten heels, pointy toe flats. (Do they pinch?) Loafers. (Do their stiff backs gash heels?) The toes: Moist or powdered? Is the second or big one longer? Are they blistered, calloused? Even or cramped? Bare or polished? Any disfiguration, fungus, bunions? The soles: Any plantar warts, bone spurs? Arches: High, mid, or collapsed? Any pronation?

How can I listen to lessons with all these other things to concentrate on? We are assigned an essay with the theme "What is school to you?"

This is my answer:

In school, I itch and get stomachaches. My mind bolts from a fish in a river up to an eagle in the sky back down to buried pebble. I get dizzy, airsick, seasick, out of control. Please someone or something come and squash or cradle all that motion. In school, I itch and get stomachaches.

But that seems, even to me as a 5th grader, inappropriate to turn in as a lesson, more like sentiments to hold close, keep private. So I write and turn in something else. It expresses a way I wish I could be. A way I wish I could think and feel. I hope that if I imagine it happening, it might actually happen:

School is a good place to learn to read, write, do equations and memorize facts. It is also a good place to learn to get along with others. Children and adults. And to respect timing: when to eat, go to the bathroom, get a drink of water. You learn you cannot just do these things any time. There are set regulations. Rules and structures are things I am fortunate enough to learn to follow in school.

I get praise for this pretend answer, so I learn making believe can go unpunished and even lead to success.

My mental murals – people, animals, vegetation, living spaces, transportation, food sources, outfits – clog up my head, so I draw them, or try to, with a sharpened yellow pencil on pads of paper Mom always has around our house. This happens alone, late at night, in my room.

That day, at school, listening to the negative views about me feels terrible. I turn red and hot. I cry, bang a wall, suck my thumb.

Another reason for my anxiety: They might mention the after-school incident with that young sub, the broom closet, my pepper spray.

But they do not.

"Your daughter does not fit in well here," one teacher says.

"She does not see things as they are, but as she thinks they are," another says.

"Anaïs Nin?" asks Mom.

"Who?"

"Anaïs Nin. Is that who you are quoting?" Mom says.

"Who?"

"The author Anaïs Nin. 'We don't see things as they are, we see things as we are.'"

"I am not familiar with him," one teacher says.

"Her," says Mom, "Anaïs Nin is a her."

"I am not familiar with her."

"We don't teach that in elementary school," another teacher says.

"But perhaps you read those kinds of things in your time away from school?" Mom says.

"Ah. No. No, Mrs. Kitto. I am not familiar with the author," the one says.

"Me either," the other says.

"Well, she is thoughtful, a little whiney," Mom says.

"Thank you, Mrs. Kitto. We are not here to talk about writers but about Meg. Her lack of participation."

I slouch, sweat through my green blouse with Indian embroidery across the scooped neckline. Tears stream down my face. My nose runs.

Mom opens the door, steps into the hall, embraces me, says, "Honey, stop crying."

She takes my hand, walks me outside, and says life is not easy. Or fair. That she has seen a few of my drawings while cleaning my room but does not want to snoop. She respects privacy, so is waiting for me to show her all of them. But what she has seen is good, very good.

Then she explains why she does not tell them about the drawings or defend me. It is because they would not hear her. That information is ammunition. Its use must be implemented shrewdly, like a military attack. She explains that sometimes information sharing at the wrong time hurts a case; defense must be implemented strategically, not shot straight from the hip. Also, never raise your voice when you disagree. Ever. That these are all ways to win. That I will understand someday. That I look very pretty in the green embroidered shirt (a gift from Aunt Gina, yes?) and those two teachers are a couple of downers. It is eighty degrees outside, and they wear nylons. She would act as crazy as them if she wore nylons on a day like today, too.

This is when she is still strong, before getting hit with that nasty illness. At this point, she still has shiny, long, lightly curled hair. She wears red lipstick, a cotton knee-length skirt, a navy blue-and-white striped sailor top, and open-toe black canvas wedged heels.

She says, "Life throws people like that our way regularly, and we have to learn to deal with them. Let's go buy flowers."

In one way my mom, Emily Kitto, my Aunt Gina, and my mother in law, Panna Shankus, are alike: They never wear panty hose. They believe they harm the leg skin, which is milky, beautiful, sensitive, and fragile. It should be given fresh air, rubbed with good creams.

Despite everything Mom says, I keep crying.

My mom rarely cries. Mostly she talks in uplifting ways. I don't know how she does it, how she manages to stay upbeat. I understand this about her now. She talks herself out of bad or sad moods, puts a positive spin on things. She could have been a preacher or a motivational speaker. She maintains enthusiasm, even in stressful situations. This can be inspiring but can also get irritating. Is it ever wrong, I want to ask Mom, to feel sad? Can't she see that, for me, if I just cry and mope for a little while, I can rebound, move from sad to happy? But that is not quite her style. She is a relentless optimist. I turn anxious. Either she does not experience anxiety or she hides it.

My favorite book at the time is *Harriet the Spy*, which is about a skillful young girl who is a detective and who lives in New York City. Mom probably was like Harriet as a child. Here is a note I write and tuck inside my copy:

I would like to be Harriet or at least her friend. I am not and cannot be as fearless and courageous as she is. Could not work with her in the field. I would trip, gasp, or cough and get caught when hiding during a spy session. I would not record properly time-sensitive information overheard on the beat.

Thoughtful – a little whiney – I think now as I re-read it. Until I get to my next line:

BUT I could do solid behind the scenes work for her – client and floor plan research, especially.

After the painful teacher meeting, Mom and I go to a diner, SHANKUS, for pudding, then buy flowers. When we get home, Dad is there. I show my parents some of my drawings made about things in school but not drawn in school.

Dad keeps saying one-word sentences followed by silence:
"Boy."
    "Man."
"Gee."
    "Wow."

Dad does not smoke pot, just sometimes talks like he does.

Mom cries. They both hug me hard and say they had no clue of my production scale.

I wonder then if Mom cries because of another reason, because it is not like her to cry when she is happily surprised.

Both are amazed by my familiarity with toe, ankle, and arch positions. I explain all foot diagrams come from a podiatry poster in our library's career counseling section. The shoe drawings. They pore over my renderings of wooden casts, repair stands, stretching pliers. Methods of sole and heel replacement, dyeing of suede, leather. Smoothing out dents and zipper and strap repair, button replacement. They ask me how I know all this?

I explain all footwear information comes from a library poster titled "Neighborhood Cobbler." It is one in a series on vanishing professions, like wet nurse, blacksmith, ice and milk deliverer.

The next morning, Mom reports me sick for school, says she is taking me on a field trip to a place she read about called Hobby Sphere. On the way, she says my sketches are so promising, maybe I can take them further. We enter Hobby Sphere, and I see just what she means. They have displays of miniature mountains, foliage-filled forests, deserts, streams. Painted granaries, lean-to dairy tool-sheds, ammo boxes. Spruces. Seasonal Aspens (green for summer and burnt orange for fall). Welcome wagons, resin cowboy toilet paper holders, mini riding boots with spurs, Japanese slippers, porcelain clogs. Miniature globes, urns, planters. Spatter frying pan, slickers with rain caps, tunics, wide skirts, vests, jeans. I feel home, sense direction. Mom has a point: I can move from drawing to building. I learn there is a name for what I want to make: dioramas. This starts the next neck of my visual junket.

I do not change schools. Mine is a public school, three blocks from our home, and is part of why we move to our neighborhood. What changes is my school's attitude. My parents, apparently, have discussions with teachers and administrators. I hear snippets of conversation.

Dad says, "They have a special child in Meg. If they do not respect this, they are idiots. If they ask her to leave, I will sue."

On Mom's end: "They are foolish, those educators. But the thing is, life is dealing with foolish people. Better Meg learn this now, in our home, with our love and support, than wait until she is off alone in the big world."

Once I get the fabrication materials and parental support, there is no stopping my diorama production. And I keep in mind what Mom says about information as ammo. Just having it is important. I don't have to share my projects at this time.

My school performance does not improve, but my mood does. I might not take in what they want to teach in class, but I am inspired to think. The Hobby Sphere gear spurs me to focus, non-judgmentally, on details. This slows me down, levels out mood surges, lapses, and swings.

I make a decision not to try and follow the ways things connect – but to take one particular thing and grip it. When the teacher writes equations on the board, I do not take in the sequence, but focus on, for example, the structure of a seven. I picture it before I go home and construct its horizontal top as a dancer's torso, the vertical bottom as her leg. Then add a bodice and tutu. Tights, pointe shoes. Hair piled up in a bun. Nail polish (dusty pink). Eyeliner. Making all this is a challenge since Hobby Sphere, great as it is, does not sell everything. But Mom helps me craft stuff from scratch.

It is a relief to focus on individual items. History becomes something I can sink my teeth into:

Sword, apron, hoof

Cannon, campfire, buffalo

Gingham

Holster, Yankee, weeds

Rope, swamp, skillet

River, pistol, bacon

This detailing stops time and movement and anchors me down. Allows me to enter a prosperous space.

Plus the stomachaches and itching decrease.

Building dioramas absorbs me. Just like the absorption I see in the yellow sponge Mom uses to wipe up spilled milk and coffee from our counter. The white and dark seep into its expansive, welcoming holes.

When I am older and look back at my constructions, I see they are more make-believe than historically accurate. They all have hills and some kind of water (lake, puddle, pond, river, faucet), even the ones that are supposed to be about pioneers heading westward through desert. I pay surgical attention to outfits (also fanciful). The tight zip-up suits and gloves. Super full skirts, boots, hats. You could call the style Little-House-on-the-Prairie-meets-Star-Trek. I mean, I say this now, but I do not remember what I was thinking then. I read all the *Little House* books and Dad loved his *Star Trek*.

The fantastic element of my constructions might seem – to the school, not my parents – annoying. I believed I was responding to lessons, exactly, but really I was mixing up the bits and pieces of what I heard and saw with my own ideas. I make strong individual objects but faulty connections.

Maybe a teacher would be surprised but happy if I came up with a diorama that accurately depicts the trajectory of a lesson.

For example: 7 x 26 = 182

Not just stopping at the seven and turning it into a ballerina.

Or a diorama of a wagon train stalled in the Badlands. The characters exhausted, shocked, confused. Filthy, limping, and bleeding. Cracked lips, sun burned, snake-bitten. Facing the mountains with terror and dismay.

Not a brawny stork airlifting the wagon train over volcanic rock, canyons, ravines.

Or replicate the photosynthesis equation: six water molecules plus six carbon dioxide molecules produce one molecule of sugar and six molecules of oxygen.

Not a vibrant sun (heavy lashes, red lips) passing through air and water to kiss, lingeringly, algae on their seabed.

Incidentally, this evolves into my first solid go-to sexual fantasy: me, on my back, in warm ocean water with legs spread. Those sun lips blowing lightly – maybe sticking a tongue briefly – between them, the lashes batting against my lower belly. I occasionally go there still.

Maybe if I had replicated accurate scenes, my teachers would have held me up as an example of a special student, a role model.

I talk with Dad about this.

He says, "Listen. Your dioramas are cartoon-like, imaginative. I like that. School does not teach you the real connections between things."

The real connections between things?

"Dad, what is that? What are those?"

"Meg, it is a process, figuring all that shit out."

Incidentally, if you wonder if moving from all this invention, contemplation, and construction to selling clothes at my aunt's shop, Simply Separate, is a step down, I take your point.

But please bear with me.

George Shankus

I'm waiting for that feeling
I'm waiting for that feeling ...
Damon Albarn, Graham Coxon

Recently, unhappy Dino gets a weekend job offer upstate from a restaurant specializing in meat. Meg is not game: "No way you go work for someone. You work for yourself, for us. You own a business, our business. You don't work for someone else's business." Her face flushes, a strand of brown hair falls down her round cheekbone.

Dino suggests she join him and start a new life outside of the city.

"Dino," she responds. "If I have to leave this city, I will kill you and then myself. Your terrific sister, Ja, can raise our orphan, Althea, and she will have more to complain about. Or Uncle Moneybags here," moving a cocked thumb toward me, "can hire nannies to take care of her."

Dino looks her in the eyes. "Diners up there eat my kind of food, Honey." He puts on a hat, goes out for a run. His second of the day.

The next two weekends, Dino travels upstate, hosting lamb roasts for this meat specialty restaurant. He returns fresh, enthused, talking rapidly about getting the lamb from a nearby farm, roasting it on a spit, and basting it with a mop from a large bucket of marinade. The appreciative customers who come early peel off and snack on crisp pieces of skin while the animal roasts. He carves the finished meat into slices and serves it with olives and peppers. For dessert, an apricot custard, heavy on the egg yolks.

I fill in for him at SHANKUS TWO since Meg feels insecure. I assure her Dino loves her and is doing what is best for the family.

What I do not say, do not have the courage to say, but want to say is this: *Dino loves you, but he is not going to be happy cooking the way he has to cook to keep SHANKUS TWO thriving in this neighborhood.* What I also want to say but do not have the courage is *Meg, I love you more, and I love you better, and I would live in this or any neighborhood with you.*

The next weekend, we get a friend to take over SHANKUS TWO. I visit Dino's new weekend digs at his invitation.

I sit at a small table in the kitchen and watch him work with the staff. Ily, the restaurant owner, works the front of the house. He did not tell me it is her joint he is working in. Ily is the "I" of *D&I: Offal.*

After he sends out his last order, we sit down to lamb belly served with a sharp sheep's milk yogurt and roasted beets. It is the best lamb belly I have ever had. I tell him our parents would be proud.

Ily takes a seat next to my brother, sips from his wine glass, and runs her hands through his hair. She asks about our family, says the book is selling well. Says she is off to meet friends for a drink.

My brother and I finish eating, take a walk, in silence, through the dense upstate woods, him swigging from a bottle of ouzo, me rehearsing what to say. Presentation is everything when it comes to getting my brother to listen.

"Dino, you are a coward and an asshole."

"I know," he says.

Silence.

Then, "She understands me. Meg doesn't."

"Does Meg know about Ily?" I ask.

Silence.

"About your relationship with her? Is it above-board?"

Silence.

"And what about Althea? What do you plan to do about her?"

Silence.

Then, "George, Meg is going to divorce me and marry one of those anorexic yoga teachers in our neighborhood. Some guy who craves our crappy soup and turns everyone against meat. You know some of those yogis only fuck once a week, on Fridays."

"Meg won't go for that, even to make you mad," I say.

"And tell me, George, how the hell would you know?"

"Dino," I say, patting his shoulder, "You seem happy here."

"I am, man. I am happy. Man, I'm a shitty dad."

"Dino, cut it out. Don't give yourself an excuse to avoid your responsibilities."

"You are right, George. Fuck. Meg is great, but Ily and I – I don't know – it is just so easy. We get along. Things are just, you know, easy with us. Meg is all into space, gardens, clothes, décor. Plus she is all over the place. I never know where she is coming from. Ily and me, we get along. We share priorities. I know, I know that sounds bullshit, that word, but it is true. We just need our restaurant. We can live in a little place with a kitchenette and two closet-sized bedrooms, you know. Her brother Bobby has an organic farm near here. Everything fits. Maybe when Althea is older, she can visit and stay in one..."

"Does Meg know, Dino?" I interrupt him.

"Aw fuck, fuck, fuck, fuck...." he says, head in his hands.

That night, I lie in bed, remembering the time in high school when Meg takes my arm on the way home from playing baseball. I remember the time I rip my pants, and she sews a patch on. Me sitting, wrapped in a towel, watching her bent over her Singer. I still have those jeans. They are folded neatly at the bottom of a chest.

I think about the difference between my brother and me: When he wants something, he makes sure to get it. I, on the other hand, tuck it inside. Or just keep it in my dreams. Dino dreams only about things he wants and plans to get. I dream about things I want but do not plan to get them. I do not connect the two – dreaming of and getting.

I fall asleep, thinking I might change that. I should at least start taking a stronger measure of control.

Meg Kitto

(with contributions from Emily Kitto)

It's not a fashion anyway
Sly Stone

In junior high school, the dioramas become more realistic because I am better skilled at combining Hobby Sphere scenes and gear with objects I make myself. I try to replicate details of our neighborhood streets and homes without injecting a personal viewpoint. Cars, bikes, buses. Subways. Parks, balls, nets, hoops. Sidewalks, chalk. Soap, cream, shampoo. Beds. Rugs, towels. Tables. Puzzles, models, cars, ships. Pitcher, knife, grater. Bread, fruit, steaks. Tins of beans, tuna, beets. Piano, guitars, pipe organ (old, worn out). Encyclopedia set.

Kids heading to school and playing during recess and lunch. A young girl just after a trip that scrapes her knee.

Here, at the injury, I stall. I consider: Does she need a band-aid? Who provides it? What kind? Is antibacterial medicine required? If yes, who applies it? Does it sting? What is its color, smell? If she is not properly treated, does the wound turn infected, pus filled, require hospitalization?

I do a little better constructing a scene of historical romance. Or, again, my idea of one from TV, movies, books, and conversations with adults. I inject myself (as a Russian princess) into the room, ask questions. What do I wear, eat? Who am I obligated to talk with at a party? Who do I want to talk to? What does he wear? Do we get close enough so I smell his breath? What is it like? Who do my parents want me to marry? Who do I want to marry? What do we eat, drink? If it is caviar and strong tea, his breath is probably pretty bad. Mine, too. Even if we are attracted to one another, would the fishy, tannic taste – the oily consistency – passing lip-to-lip, possibly tongue-to-tongue, tongue-to-throat, be memorably offputting? Would that jeopardize our love in the future? Would that overcome any heat of attraction?

How are our plates, goblets, cups, and cutlery sanitized? (Are they?) How do we wash our bodies and hair? Who does the washing? What is the scent of soap? How do women deal with body hair? Who prepares our food? How is it cleaned? Who serves it? Who folds the sheets, readies the beds? What do we use for toilet paper? What is its texture?

I do not do a great job, answering those questions, but do deal with the clothes. Can easily picture me, my mom, and aunt in ball gowns, face powder, and wigs. Maybe it would not be so pleasant to wear, with the corsets and stockings. I worry about the undergarments and wonder if they scratch. But I can picture us in the Russian outerwear, like in *Anna Karenina*. I can see us even enjoying dressing up. I cannot imagine the fathers and uncles I know wearing what I understand men wore then: the waistcoats, ties, heels, wigs. Most men I know (Dad, uncles, neighbors) wear pressed pants and shirts with ties to work. At home, or a party, they are in Levi's, flannel shirts, hiking boots, or sneakers. I cannot even picture my friend Leslie's dad, the stylish doctor, who is usually in some kind of suit and a tie over a shirt with an interesting print. Flowers and paisley sometimes even. Flat slip-on shoes. But even someone stylish like him, I cannot imagine in a wig and heels.

I understand men sometimes dress this way now as a form of self-expression or to be festive or to make a point. I know people like that now but did not encounter them growing up. But, I mean, I don't think of that attire as something a regular American guy would put on to go to a party in order to flirt or speak with an older relative or powerful person about opportunity the way they do in classic romantic novels.

What this tells me is that, historically, men and women's fashions change so differently.

Something shifts in 10th grade when my folks and I visit Uncle Ralph, a professor, at his college campus, a school my parents want me to attend. We walk the grounds, sit in on lectures of my potential majors (design, art history), and eat lunch at the student union. I eavesdrop on student conversations (pot, politics, parties) and listen to Uncle Ralph talk about the student body. Generally, he says, they have "fun" but are serious and engaged in ways that impress and worry him: political activism, drugs, ecosystems, sex, protests.

The information lands me in unfamiliar territory.

I long to understand these people, a few years older than I am but worlds away. (Hard to believe I will soon be a college student, perhaps living among them.) I do not yet connect with them. They seem further away from me than the *Little-House-on-Prairie* characters or the westward traveling settlers in my dioramas. Maybe because I worry about their opinion. I know make-believe people will never see or respond to what I make. But these people might. I still worry. When I return home, I assemble my gear and try putting together something of my, maybe, soon-to-be classmates:

Tambourines, guitars

Denim

Rainbow prints

Head bands

Bare arms, long hair

Toe rings

Temporary Shelters

PEACE & FREEDOM scrawled across bare chests, cheeks, along arms and on the front of t-shirts

Then, after diagramming those elements, I try to inject elements of character/behavior:

Blurry eyes

Mud, locked lips

Needles, slump, drool

Marches, rallies, locked arms

These dioramas are not sure-footed and seem phony to me. Maybe because I feel embarrassed. I wonder who am I to make up things about the students? They are actual people. Strangers. Not school lessons, neighbors, book, movie or TV characters. Plus I fall a little in love with them. All of them. And really want them to love me back. I feel nervous they might not, so I shy away from constructing anything with meaning that might be considered unflattering.

"Bias," says Dad when I tell him. "You are aware in your depictions you have a bias."

The real connection between things?

Figuring out what this means sticks with and disturbs me.

It becomes a big deal.

Individual objects are there, free standing. Anyone looking can connect them in his or her own way. But once I try to make meaning or invent a story about something real, unfamiliar, and not from a book or lesson or myself, I inject an opinion and risk missing the target. Maybe it is something only very smart and well-qualified people should do. Not me.

All that time in elementary school, I wondered if some neurological disorder prevents me from connecting the discreet pieces of information (equations, time lines, grammar). Now I wonder if it is psychological. An aversion to/fear of linkage. Because stating connections, even suggesting them, is an act of privilege.

I mean, I think.

Have I earned the privilege?

If no, who am I to state things?

If yes, how? How have I earned it?

I am not selling myself short; my self-esteem is actually quite high.

Just asking a question. I think it is important.

The kids in my high school – including me – have strong opinions on a range of things as if they are equally important (shoes, make up, clothes, humor, sports, political parties, music).

This heavy judgment makes me uncomfortable, yet I completely fall in its trap. I do not make connections. I follow them.

I follow fashion "rules." I make sure I wear the exact shoes the cool kids wear, put a light gloss on my lips, cheerlead, barely brush my long hair. I am embarrassed (really embarrassed) my dad votes Republican. Ask Mom to please pack simple sandwiches on sliced bread for my bag lunch, not a millet bun with tomato, basil and brie. Not a container of ratatouille.

I have conversations with her about judgment. When is it right and when not? She does what she normally does when I go off on a tangent or over focus: She distracts me. Hobby Sphere is a great past example. Now, she slips short messages or story lines into my lunch box or sweater pocket. This starts a while after the dioramas. She, as you know, is impressed with my visual skills but worries about my language development, so she provides reading material for practice. In addition to helping divert my attention.

– I –

The notes start off simple:

Have a great day!
I Love You.
Purple is your color!
Love the sweater you wear today. It has a slightly loose button, so be careful.

They evolve into a series of sentences. One or two per day that make up a story. For example:

In a park, on a bench, sits a man.
Just because he is alone, do not think that he is lonely.
He eats a sandwich, watches birds.
Looks forward to playing handball with buddies this evening.
He finishes eating, folds up the sandwich wrapper, slips it into his briefcase.

Stands up, walks eight blocks to the bookstore. A bird follows him closely and rubs her beak against the back of his calf.

He wears pressed khakis.

He enters the bookstore, browses. When he exits, there next to its entrance is the bird.

She hops after him.

He walks ten blocks to get a coffee. The outside tables are full. So, he enters the cafe, sits, reads the paper, and sips his pour over. Black, two sugars.

He pays his bill, leaves a tip, exits.

There, just to the side of the entranceway, stands the bird. He crouches down, looks her in the eye. She has, for a bird, long eyelashes and interesting eyes.

The eyes remind him of Maria, his wife, his late wife.

He sees, around the bird's neck, what looks like a silver necklace.

It isn't a necklace. It is the bird's feathers that for some reason have a color in the shape of a necklace.

It is a near replica of the necklace he gave to Maria the first birthday he knew her.

The bird bats her eyelashes, gently pecks at his loafer.

They lock eyes.

He holds out his finger.

She hops onto it.

Pecks his arm lightly.

Hops onto his shoulder.

Gently runs her beak along his neck.

They walk home in the late afternoon sunlight.

– END –

This is fifteen days' worth of notes. I still have the fifteen pieces of paper. Mom writes in ink on rice paper. These are the first stories I ever read by Mom.

The real connection between things?

I grow increasingly aware of global issues – serious and sad – most of which I never "see" in real life (just in magazines and on TV) or hear about in adult conversations. As carefully as I can, I try to detail some of it:

Eyeballs. Chains. Ankles

Burned buildings, trees

Smashed plumbing

Soggy books, photographs

Shattered glass (windows, jars)

Single Shoe

Bent backs

Looted cupboard

Towels, dirt

Mattress

Dented swing set

Dogs sniffing, birds circling

Dolls, headless

Flower bouquets

A mother on the floor, fetal position, after her son heads off
to war

A family, arms around one another, looking at their flooded
fields

Strategic planning

Foot soldiers

But I sense these attempts at meaning injection are things
to keep to myself. I ask Dad, who says there is something about
letting some things out in public and keeping others private. He
says sometimes you can hurt a cause or diminish information by
clumsy expression. That I have a long time to hone connecting
skills. Also, in his opinion, most people, unfortunately, hit the
peak of social and political awareness as late teenagers or young
adults. Maybe because at this age people oversimplify. That
the interest should not diminish after but that, in many cases,
it does. He is not sure if this has to do with laziness, arrogance,
lack of interest, or the difficulty of dealing with the complexity
and the nuances of all the different viewpoints.

But he tells me I have to keep on trying. That I should hold
onto a goal of one day making connections and sharing them
with the public.

"Dad, why?"

"Because," he says, "Our world needs our participation, even
if flawed. People have to. We just do, Meg. If not you, who?"

I know, then and there, I am absolutely going to let Dad down.

An example of a personal moment I make into a diorama:

Two people, a man (corduroys, loafers) and a young girl (scout uniform, loafers) are just turning from a school hallway and into a broom closet. The man has his hand on the door, and it is half open. His other hand touches the child's shoulder. They stand at the closet entrance, looking inside. It captures an instant pre-story.

An autobiographical story by me:

This is the day the substitute asks me to put aside my make-up math work and help him retrieve cleaning supplies from the broom closet. Part of me wants to decline, and part of me cannot not resist saying yes. I follow him to the broom closet, feeling (I have to admit it) a charge when he lightly rubs his fingers under my chin. But something kicks in, and I, armed with the pepper spray, use it, run away, and hear the screams – "Meg! Meg! What did you... Why?" – which makes me feel horrible. I hurt the substitute, poor man, who does not even have a secure job. I never tell anyone because I do not understand it. I worry if I tell someone they will leap to judgment, and I am not convinced there is a case here to judge. I understand the viewpoint that this decision is terrible and possibly endangers children. Perhaps my silence leaves him free to lure them in closets. But it is just as likely he was harmless. We were at the broom closet entrance, not behind a closed door or in a cupboard, trunk, or basement. The thing is, maybe he just wanted me to get something down from a shelf or get a new eraser for the chalkboard or get something to sweep up the crumbs on the floor from the in-class birthday party we had that day (It was Clark's birthday.) I am relieved to take a break from my ink-stained page of scribbled make-up math, which is illegible with crossed out equations and help. And I grow up learning the value of tasks. Mom believes light housework like sweeping, cooking, and folding, are good for concentration. So it makes sense I would agree to help tidy up, a request that would be made by Mom or also an affectionate uncle. And you might say the fact he did not report the fact I sprayed him to the school or my parents was an admission of guilt. But he might have just thought it would stir up trouble and realize he did not have a case to stand on. He was a very young man. I go back to this and still do not know how to think about it.

Why did my parents make me carry pepper spray?

We moved into a neighborhood that had some problems with street crime. Not a lot but some. And they, and the other parents on the block, all agreed it would be a good idea for kids to carry pepper spray. No one had guns or knives or anything – just protective pepper spray so you could defend yourself but not harm anyone, just in case you might be wrong. No one gets seriously hurt with spray. The effect is harsh but temporary.

Spray lets you protect yourself without inflicting harm, without the danger of serious repercussions if you happen to be wrong.

The incident gets me thinking: Physical affection, touching, was not always so taboo. One of my favorite teachers, Mr. Lefanowitz, used to plunge his finger into boys' necks if they misbehaved. "Lefanowitz Finger," they called it. They shrieked, but the finger got them under control. They all loved him. And those boys were unruly, let me tell you that. And I know it calmed me down if a teacher came over to me at my desk when I was itchy, confused, and upset and crouched down, whispered, "Are you okay, Meg?" in my ear, and stroked my head or back. Those things really help. So I just don't know how to think of what happened with the sub.

Mom's stories change from short lines to longer pieces that are fleshed out. She says she writes them to help me combine two kinds of thinking: a path and a tower. She elaborates:

Path Thinking: the kind that moves along, one thing following another.

Tower Thinking: the kind that stops time and packs things in, floor to ceiling.

Sometimes these two combine in ways that make it hard to separate.

She says that both ways of thinking are good mental exercises and that if you practice both, they, at times, come magically together.

She also says that I do not always need to decide between things. That living and thinking in between things is viable, if not always socially accepted.

Another example of a story she puts, neatly folded, in the bottom of my lunch box in high school:

Portal
By Emily Kitto
For Meg
Darling,
Get your head out of
the real world and back in
the clouds.
For a while!
Love, Mom

– II –

My parents are infected. Visual toxicity. They do not permit me to see.

Sightless, they hope I will develop an acute sense of hearing. Why? Sound leads to space, and once this world is gone, which it may be soon, our hope lies there.

Mom and Dad put me in places (trunks, cupboards, closets, containers) that are hidden, always comfortable. They dress me in things (goggles, scarves, ear muffs, bear suits, hoods, masks) to cover my eyes. In those spaces, behind those accessories, I am safe, protected, and able to hone things auditory.

My small size makes concealment and mobility easy. I travel in pet purses and bags. Mom has an extensive supply of carriers. Sometimes she lets me choose the tote. (I run my hands along the individual pieces of her collection and feel the leather, cloth, wool, or vinyl.) And Dad, the sportsman (golfer, swimmer, biker), owns multiple duffels.

Unsurprisingly, my listening is fine-tuned. I hear a knock, giggle, ring, or voice and guess who or what is behind it. For example, I know my aunt's door knock versus our neighbor's. I know the mailman's footsteps versus the milkman's. Know when Mom turns the oven to 350 degrees or to broil. I discern her way of playing our piano as opposed to when her friend Ed plays. Both experiment with extended, questioning arpeggios and strong chords: simple, sure, combative. But Mom's playing is calm, confident. Ed is a showman. I know what kind of food she puts in her cart at the grocery store (potatoes, jarred peppers, canned tuna).

When we come home from the market and she takes me out of a tote and puts me in the drawer or under the bed, I sometimes hear her on the piano. She is more experimental without Ed. Starts off tinkling the keys for easy up and down scales before going to edgier thirds and fifths to pounding octaves. I have never seen a piano, but I listen and, sometimes when I get her in the right mood, she lets me ask questions. Music, she believes, is the most important thing.

Sometimes her friend visits. They discuss husbands, music, toxic lawns, trees, and asphalt in our neighborhood.

I know when she runs water in the kitchen to wash dishes or when she makes tea or noodles, as opposed to running water for my bath. Hot water for dishes, cold for the food and drink, and in-between for me.

I know the mood she is in when she says "Get up" by the rasp in her voice. Some mornings, it is eager. Others, it sounds exhausted. Those days, I hear her say how she does not have long. She and Dad think they keep secrets from me, but of course they cannot since I hear them, even when I am tucked inside a shoebox and they are in another room behind a closed door.

I can hear when we have mice in the house, even on a different floor. I hear Mom and Dad agree they do not want me to see the sad, grimy, and evil of the world. (Those three words – "sad," "grimy," and "evil" – are maybe Dad's favorite or at least most common description of what goes on at work, on our block, in stores, or even in our driveway.)

"She will never see real trees. At least we can spare her the sight of these fake ones."

"What passes for cars and bikes these days is just appalling. They are not real. They are made to look real, but we know they cannot function. Just sit on our streets and sidewalks: fake reassurance, bad sculptures."

This I know: Mom and Dad are worried. They are also prepared with a solid escape plan. The reason we have not left, I understand, from listening and not being told, is because they are not convinced any other place is cleaner or safer than where we are now.

I hear them agree, though, that if the poison completely overtakes our town, country, or world, perhaps their daughter – that is, me – is the future. Because only I will be aurally prepared. Sound is a portal to the divine, and though my body is shot, like everyone else's, my ears will get me there and hopefully help me bring others.

– END –

Mom knows exactly how to help me deal with pressure: distraction.

I accidentally turn the story in with my biology lab report.

"Is Emily Kitto your mom?" asks my bio teacher, returning it.

"Yes."

"Emily and I go way back."

"Really?"

"Yes. I missed her wedding."

"Wow."

"She is scientifically astute. You can tell her I said so."

"Uhm, I will. Thank you."

"Maria," she says. "Tell her hello from Maria."

"Ok."

Emily Kitto

Sitting on my own not by myself
Cat Stevens

I get sick in my mid 40's but, truthfully, start feeling lousy years earlier. Move between denial ("I am not tired") to disbelief ("I must be making all this pain up...") to blaming myself for being rickety, dramatic, and a sinner.

Can illness be a gift? Can loss?

One doctor suggests my poor health – the pain, the fatigue – is linked to my father's early death. (I was six.) The doctor thinks this because of the traumatic event itself, together with ways he sees me responding to it (squashing down feelings, thoughts, questions). He tries to help and encourages me to talk, draw, build things with blocks, and form shapes with clay. But I do not engage with those activities. I hear him tell Mom that if I do not start to express things, they will sour, rot, infect. But he does not know what goes on in my head. He does not know secret things I do to soothe myself. I make up songs, scenes, people. Why does he want me to share my private thoughts in public?

I have a reason to keep things close. Revealing secrets and demons might give them energy, fuel them to structure, swell, accelerate. I am not sure if this is because I hear and love the Pandora's Jar story or if I love the story because it speaks to something already brewing within me.

I hear the Pandora Story (and learn it is a jar she unlocks, not a box) from my nextdoor neighbor Liz, who is the big sister of my best friend, Maria. One Halloween, she tells us the story, a few versions, and re enacts it with us, combined with the Hansel and Gretel fairy tale.

Maria (lederhosen, cap) is Hansel, and I (smock, braids) am Gretel. We both wear ankle boots and carry croutons to toss onto lawns, porches, and sidewalks. Liz makes the croutons. They are excellent – with salt, pepper, a dash of rosemary, and a light douse of honey. We tell her these are too good to toss out and waste, even on birds. This pleases Liz, who says we should go ahead and eat the croutons because they are better for us than candy, especially on a school night. She also says she doubts croutons do birds any good. Liz loves birds, even then.

Several years later she successfully leads a neighborhood campaign to protect them from predatory cats. She explains letting cats roam outside, especially at night, means birds get attacked, mauled, killed. She makes and distributes a poster:

Indoor/Outdoor Cats. The top shows a series of cats indoors: One sleeps on a desk, one looks out a kitchen window, and one plays with a ball of string in a library. The middle shows assorted birds (a bird watcher might know the species, but I just notice their colors: red, black, gray, yellow) in various positions (flying, perching, pecking) on and around trees, fences, and bushes. The point being that the birds and cats appear healthy and happy as long as the cats are in and the birds are out. The bottom portion is dark and torrid. It depicts a cat, feral and fanged, pouncing on a bird. It shows a little bird carcass, post cat attack, ripped apart. There is a soundtrack of a bird chirping and singing alternated with pained, high-pitched shrieks.

Because of her educational and persuasive campaign, our neighborhood comes together for a series of meetings. A mother reminds us of the time a cat saved her son, who was playing in the yard, from a vicious dog attack. "Yes," Liz responds. "Cats are wonderful. No one is anti-cat." But the mother persists. If the cat had been indoors, she would not have been able to frighten the dangerous dog.

"Yes," Liz responds, "but if you had been supervising your child, the dog would not have had access to her."

This gets them into a large discussion about child supervision. Is it ever safe to leave a child unattended? Is it overprotective not to? After a long meeting, neighbors bond. They agree children can be protected easier than birds. The group votes to prohibit outdoor cats, even if they have bells on their necks. (Ineffective.) Liz, hoping we show unity and spread the word, passes out two buttons for us to wear:

1) **KEEP CATS IN**

2) **PRO-BIRD.**
   NOT
   ANTI-CAT.

We enlist trainers to work with the cats that are accustomed to being outdoors but no longer allowed to be. This is a completely different story that is only in part successful.

Back to that Halloween night. Liz is Pandora. She wears a long dark wig, a sheer ankle-length white nightgown over a pink leotard and tights, flat gladiator sandals, and strings of thick clay necklaces and bracelets. (Pandora, she explains, is originally made of clay.) She slings her trick-or-treat net over her shoulder and cradles a jar filled with earth, pebbles, plastic insects, mice, and reptiles in her arms. Nestled at the jar's bottom, below all of the dark matter, she places a fresh red rose that is covered with and protected by cloth (a family handkerchief that is hand-embroidered).

Liz tosses out bits from her organic and plastic-matter jar mixture.

A neighbor sees this and asks us please not to dirty his lawn. Liz tells him her dirt and pebbles are eco-friendly (unlike the weed killer she sees him use) but admits he has a point about the plastic matter and promises to retrieve every bit at sunrise.

At the end of the night, Maria and I have empty pockets, and Liz has an empty jar, except for the rose bundle. She asks us to stand with her on the lawn between our houses. It is dark, and the street is empty. My parents trust Liz, so they do not worry I am not home, even though it is late and I am six. House lights are on and so are a few streetlights and several stars and the perfect half moon. Liz asks us to hold hands in a small circle, appreciate things good, acknowledge things bad, declare neighbor unity. She then unwraps her cloth and reveals the rose. It is fresh, red, fragrant. To me, it is the most perfect, beautiful object I have ever seen. Of course, it is not simply the object; it is the context: the moon, the mood, Liz, Maria, our costumes, our croutons and candy. She brings the flower to her nose and breathes deeply. Then places it beneath each of our noses, asks us to do the same. In a voice that is deep, accented, and not her normal one, she says, "After Pandora lets all that ugliness escape the jar, she opens it again and finds one more thing. It is a big thing, maybe the biggest: hope. This rose signifies hope. I drop it between our front lawns, wishing both our families a year of bounty and solidarity."

She tosses the flower onto the lawn dividing our homes and hums a few bars of something, reminding me of Volga Boat Song (which I learned the week before at piano).

It ends as an eerie, exciting night.

When Dad is killed, just a short time after, the memory of that Halloween turns spine-chilling.

At first, it is hard for me not to blame Liz, Maria, Hansel, Gretel, their dad, and step-mom. Pandora.

Just think of the dirt, the plastic spiders, mice, and beetles. Believe, for a time, they are a curse. I forget about the rose as a sign of hope. Or do not focus on it until later.

Liz, Maria, and their parents are great comforts to me and Mom.

We never discuss the Halloween night's possible connection to Dad's death.

Liz, though, continues to tell us different versions of the Pandora Story (which, she maintains, is ultimately hopeful).

One particular take convinces me she reads my mind when it comes to my experience with the doctor.

Or maybe the story explains my behavior with him.

Pandora is a young girl whose body contains a mixture of beauty and ugliness. ("The jar," says Liz, "is a metaphor.") She holds it all tightly inside. Sometimes these elements inside make her feel buoyant, beautiful. Others, they hurt, press, infect. She does not know whether to keep them in or let them out. One evening, she decides to let just a single one out. She worries, though, about regulation. She worries that once she releases one little thing all of the others will follow – and not in a way that is orderly or portioned – but in a manner where everything will shoot (she pictures a comet) or surge (she pictures a waterfall).

But she has been called a worrywart her entire life, so she decides, for once, to put doubts aside and eject a single, separate something. (She imagines it as the smallest Lego piece, red.) She tries to execute this, but it bolts, surges. The energy stream, which is completely out of her hands, blasts open an expansive exit space. Pandora is helpless in this gush of unregulated migration. These things leaving her and going into the world generate lots of problems. She regrets not keeping her thoughts and feelings bound up inside because then she would just be harming herself, not others. She would be willing to do that – to hurt herself as a sacrifice for others. Now it is too late for that. Everything is wrecked, and even though Pandora feels momentarily light, airy, and a bit depleted, she is an emotional mess. And her body feels hard, steely. As bad as those things felt inside her, they did not approach the anguish of something she never knew before. Guilt. Guilt is the worst. It makes her want to die.

This is a misunderstanding of the Pandora story since it edits out the rose and the hope at the end. I could add it and maybe say she looks at the sky or an ocean and senses hope.

But I do not. I focus on the mistake she makes of letting things out, and I take this with me to the doctor.

I shove things down, even tiny pinpricks, before they form, before I can understand or take them seriously. It is my youthful coping mechanism.

Problems shared are problems multiplied.

Later I learn that you do not need Big Hopes. Even a little bit of hope can turn out to be mighty. But that comes a few years later.

My father dies when I am six. It was a shooting accident in the woods, up north, bow and arrow hunting, with a group of friends. Technically not gun-shooting season, but some-one shoots anyway. An illegal shot kills dad. He is twenty-six. I am six.

It takes me out of the stream of things or puts me in a differ-ent stream.

What do I remember about him? Not sure. My heart and head and shoulders expand when I think of him. I remember his hugs. Or think I do.

As I said, I keep my feelings private but in ways that feel comforting, not painful. I incubate my sadness. Spending time with it helps me transform the feeling from something oppres-sive, thick, heavy, into pictures, songs, stories that lighten me, my mood and body.

When I think of Dad, it is mostly as a boy. He dies so young, and I remember so little but so vividly. I have memories (khaki pants, shock of blond hair, whispers of stories in my ear) and pictures.

For a while, I truly believe Liz is in my head and start to think Dad is, too.

Growing up, I feel outside – feel I am outside – watching my-self. Trying to become a person I think Dad would want me to be. In any situation, I pictured an angel, or Dad, looking down at me from above, and my behavior is always designed to please or impress that eye. Never alone, I cannot just be, I must perform. For Dad. I feel good when I do well, bad if I mess up.

I spend a lot of time thinking about communicating with Dad. At least as much time as living in my day-to-day life. He is there, watching over me, there for me to talk to. I would way rather communicate with Dad than the doctor. With Dad, in fact, why do I need that doctor?

Having Dad around makes me work hard to be clean, neat, efficient, kind, even in private. I really never am completely in private. I have Dad.

But problems arise when I start wanting to kiss boys or touch myself. I do not want Dad watching any of that. We come up with an agreement. At first he looks away, but over time, he disappears into wherever he is because he senses I no longer need him to watch so carefully out for me. He still does but only when he senses something is wrong or I am around people or when I specifically ask him to be there.

George Shankus

Now that just gave my heart a throb
to the bottom of my feet
Robbie Robertson

I decide to make an unplanned visit when Meg (yellow v-neck dress and gladiator sandals) tells me Dino is not communicating with her.

I say I want to help.

She says she does not want help, just facts.

This puts me in a bad position. I know about Ily, and Meg does not. Or sort of does. But how much, really, do I learn during that visit I make at Dino's invitation? Maybe I need to surprise him to learn the real story.

This approach, like some of my best business deals, requires a combination of subterfuge and face-to-face conversation. I know that today he travels north. Now I know what this means: to Ily. Her meat, customers, hoop earrings. Her restaurant with its tasteful, rustic interior: logs, linen, organ, fireplaces, heavy cutlery, thick-legged chairs and tables.

I trail him. See him stop for an egg roll at a breakfast cart on his way to the station. I watch him enter the station and catch my reflection in a store window. It is predatory, heaving. I am not proud of my behavior. Yet I am still practical. Sometimes, assessing movements of a family member (with the close history, the past and present interaction) muddles and distracts. Establishing distance helps a person, me anyway, to collect reliable data.

Late that night, I drive north in my car.

The last time Dino and I speak, it is about a movie. The restaurant keeps him busy. He has little time for film, but he sees this on cable. The movie is a romance. Ily falls asleep. Dino calls, complaining, not about Ily falling asleep but about the romance. He wants to see a romance about a regular guy. Not about a guy who falls for a woman with chunky ankles and a good personality. Who sends that woman flowers regularly. Whose idea of a romantic evening is filling a bathtub with bubbles and surrounding it with candles. That is some female idea of a guy. What Dino wants from a romance is this: A guy falls for a tall, gazelle-legged, big-breasted woman. Sexually voracious. A lingerie wearer. The big breasts are really important. She falls for him, too. She is not vain, psychotic, anorexic, dizzy, or cocaine addicted. He is tired of movies about hot women who are nasty, conniving, sick, and stupid. Tired of movies where unattractive women get men to see through to their inner beauty.

"Guys don't see through any damn thing. We either feel it –
Pow! – or we don't," he says.

"Dino, you are such an asshole. I cannot believe we come
from the same family."

"Hey, I say what I feel, not what I mean. Listen, I am just
talking about what I want from a *movie*. Not real life. I mean, it
is not as if Ily's ankles are tiny. She stands in Crocs all day, her
ankles puff up, you know. And it is not as if her breasts are,
I mean, it is not as if...."

"Dino, I really don't want to hear this. "

"Yea, coming from Mr. Pure-and-Simple."

"Shut up, Dino. Just shut the fuck up."

I get to their place just after dawn. Too early to pop in. Park
my car near their home, take a walk in the woods. Reluctantly.
I am uncomfortable in forests and am aware this attitude is un-
American, un-masculine. The fact is I do not like density in
nature. In a city, it is terrific. I enjoy jam-packed streets, subways,
theaters, bars, lobbies, diners. That density is not static. But
trees just stand still, hiding who knows what. I am not anti-
nature. Give me any kind of water, and I am home. Sailing,
diving, rowing, fishing, swimming. Give me a mountain to hike
or ski, starting high up, looking down, out, skyward. It is just
woods I have a problem with.

I walk for a nervous hour and enjoy, admittedly, the smell:
fresh, clean, piney. When I return to the driveway, thankful to
be going indoors, even if it is to Dino's trailer, a pick-up truck

brushes the mailbox and almost me right next to it. It stops. A man with long hair, psychedelic print t-shirt, and thong sandals steps out. He is not tall, and he is not good looking, but then he is not short or ugly either. Just a guy dressed like an old hippie, with a chin beard in rimless glasses. He shakes his head, rubs his cheek, and says, "Man, man, I am so fucking, man...." He cannot finish the sentence. I take a deep breath of not pine but pot. He gestures to the joint in his hand and says he is taking his prescription medical marijuana. He says he comes by Dino and Ily's in the morning for informal breakfast munchies like potatoes, eggs, and mushrooms. He has no problem talking now. I nod my head, remembering never liking anything about pot, the smell or the high. Beer is different. I like both the smell and the high, the taste and the fizz, and I am thinking along these lines when I feel dizzy and fall, bam, on ground. Turn my head to the side, see his toes peeping out of the sandals. They are clean, even toes, not gnarled or dirty the way you might expect from an old hippie. That is the last thing I remember before blacking out.

I wake up, feeling as if I am in outer space.

A face with red, puffy under-eye bags, cracked lips, and carefully groomed blond hair breathes down on me. I can see but not move.

"What happened?" the face asks.

"She just went down," says the pothead.

"He. I am a he. He," I try to say but cannot yet speak.

"This is a man, not a she," says the blond. Wearing a striped shirt with the name "ED" above the right pocket. I see there is a bus behind him. I guess he is the driver.

A load of warmly dressed, well fed people surround me.

"Stand back! Here comes the doctor," says Ed to them.

"Do you mind if I examine you?" asks a brisk voice. A head, also blond-haired, is over me. Ed is gone.

No, I do not mind at all, I try to say, but I cannot speak, so no words come out.

She pulls out a joint, asks do I want some.

NO, I badly want to say, to yell. I want to add I have not seen this much pot since college, but I just close my lips tightly together.

She looks at me, tokes.

"Historically, I make my most accurate diagnosis when I have a quick toke."

Historically, I do not go to doctors who are potheads, I want to respond but am unable to.

She pinches the joint, tucks it in her chest pocket, tells me my pupils are not dilated, which is a good thing.

She runs her hands along my skull and shoulders, kneads my neck. Something releases.

"There. You are fine," she says.

I do feel better and respect an urge to share with someone the bizarreness of what happened.

"Listen, Doc, I think I got a contact high. I drove up here from the city. Got here before anyone was up. Took a walk. Came back to my brother's. This guy came up, smoking his medical marijuana after almost ramming into me with his truck, and I took one whiff and fell –"

"Contact high is a myth," she interrupts, authoritatively. "It is scientifically impossible."

Then it hits me like a ton of bricks: This woman, in crystal clarity, encapsulates why I hate doctors. Arrogance, drugs, rigidity. I am not wrong, after all, to miss my annual physicals. And I am going to tell Meg to chill out on those annual mammograms. Eating well, having sex, and working out does more for my health than any physical with a moron. I close my eyes, feeling good, feeling right.

I wake up on my brother's couch, still feeling good. Ily stands in the kitchen, drinking a glass of water. She wears her white chef top with loose-fitting blue pants, yellow Crocs. The color makes me think of Meg's yellow v-neck dress. That is not true. I do not need a color to make me think of Meg. Ily walks toward me, offers a sip from her glass, asks how I am, runs her palm over my forehead. This is the first person, besides Ed, I meet here not toking. I breathe easy. She tells me Dino is at work, that I slept for an hour and that we have an appointment with a doctor later this afternoon. My mood shifts from relaxed to heated. I want to express myself: *Doctors are assholes and unimportant. I will not go to a fucking doctor this afternoon. No Way.* This is all on the tip of my tongue until she gestures to a table laid out with a colorful lunch: sweet breads, lemons, arugula, tomatoes, pumpernickel. This pulls me in, helps me realize I am starving. Despite my hunger fog, though, I am crystal clear on one thing: Thank God for Ily because her presence structures the possibility of Meg and me truly being together.

Meg Kitto

Nothing Compares
2 U
Prince

In college, I lose interest in diorama construction. The connecting issue grows overwhelming and leaves me perspiring, panicked, just how I feel, pre-diorama, in elementary school. I never thought that feeling would come back but, boom, it does.

I move on and welcome the change. I make friends, earn solid grades, learn that doing well academically takes way less effort than constructing imagined worlds. My dioramas entail hard thinking, invention, love; all this goes into my villages, landscapes, characters and their gear. Not to mention the technical challenges: applying polish to a pinkie nail, replicating bananas that are overly ripe with brown streaks as well as basic yellow, getting the skin tone of an injured soldier. The grades, in contrast, mean shutting off deep thinking and just following a system. I realize my problem with school is that I try too hard to pay attention. Once I turn my mind off, I just answer the questions and do fine. Anyway, this makes it easier for me to socialize and to do extra-curricular things, like join film and drama clubs.

My drama club involvement starts with costumes. I help choose and alter outfits for the actors. I learn how important get ups are for the performance. If the actor is great, the costumes enhance. (I love it when the word "great" is linked to dramatic roles. She was *a great* Medea or Blanche or Hedda. He was a *great* Lear, Loman, Danton.) If the actor does not emote or, maybe worse, overdoes it or cannot carry a tune, you at least can look at and be convinced by tailored trousers, work boots, velvet slippers, interesting sleeves, hemlines, hats. The first production I work on is *The Music Man*. I alter one of the high-necked, tight-waisted, flouncy skirts for Marion (Madame Librarian). I polish Harold Hill's spats and press his necktie and suit.

I smudge dirt on faces, mess up hair, put holes in pants, and rip dress sections when we do *Grapes of Wrath*.

For Orwell's *1984*, I find standard button-up shirts and loose pants. I help with make up: greasy hair and pasty skin.

This bolsters my interest in clothing construction.

I once suggest to Dino that clothes and costumes for actors are maybe something like food presentation. A good meal can be heaped on a plate and still taste fantastic, but if it is arranged nicely, it enhances. He says that lots of people suggest that presentation is important, but the emphasis on food and visuals is bullshit. Arrangement has nothing to do with meal quality. Pretty arrangements that taste mediocre are unacceptable, and that is where so many restaurants now go. Tasty food that looks messy is just fine. It does not make the meal and the chef failures.

Dino does not think abstractly. I spend a lot of time with him saying, "Well, I mean not always, but sometimes you could look at it that way. I mean maybe."

Another part to this is Dino dislikes the idea of eating with eyes. Some chefs say this – that "We eat with our eyes." This really bothers him. He feels there is a place for this, but it has gotten out of control. So that opinion might cause the over reaction, the "bullshit" comment.

He is also not an advocate of the blind-food experience that some eateries advocate now, where meals are eaten in pitch dark or while diners wear eye masks, supposedly so they just focus on the taste and texture.

Anyway, after working on productions, I re-examine the outfits I make for my diorama figures and remember how much time and thought I put into them. Clothes and I have a strong history. You can see my interest level was high: The pioneer on an Iowa ranch has a dress made of muslin. The beads on a hippie's bracelets are thought out, and the color and pattern are wise. A princess wears tulle and silk. The cowboys with boots and leather vests. The princes wear pumps, tights, exposed socks, and knickers. The pipe organ player in a stiff suit with shoulders raised and torso hunched over the keyboard.

Yes, I am accurate at clothing construction, but what is the greater purpose?

I knew I was going to let Dad down.

Full Disclosure:

Some people are picky about food or exercise. I have a tough stomach and don't care about physical movement that much, but as I grow older, I become particular about how I dress. I cannot leave the house if I am not wearing something that expresses what I want it to. I am not proud of being this way.

Mom has a hard time eating, especially since she gets sick. She, too, is always careful about what she wears, maybe because of her sister, Gina. Or maybe Gina gets her fine clothing sense from Mom.

I do not care how other people dress unless they come to me for professional or friendly advice.

I take a stab at making clothes for people, not dolls and figures. Sort through various patterns and purchase thread, material. I reacquaint myself with mom's Singer. Sewing is not as fun as diorama construction, and I am not as good at it. I mean, the pieces are nothing that I would try to sell a store or to another person. They really aren't very good at all. I enjoy working with my hands and understand handwork enough to understand that I am not a skilled craftsperson.

Nothing like Aunt Gina's friend The Seamstress. But even more important than my mediocre handwork is that I lack another quality crucial for a great clothing designer: speed. Great designers get a sense of culture, and culture changes rapidly.

I do not move fast.

As you can probably tell.

Thoughtful, a little whiney.

Fashion moves fast. Designers have to catch the wave, the moment, the zeitgeist, but understand that it lasts only fleetingly. Then they have to scout out the next one coming. Again, this is something The Seamstress manages so well.

Speed lies outside my skill set. Shopping does, too.

I always shopped with Mom and never realized how heavily I relied on her to help choose clothes and fend off the sales people. Wait, bad choice of words. Mom never fends them off. She deals with them firmly, politely, elegantly. She keeps them at bay. I just feel scared and helpless and pushed into a series of bad decisions. Mom is an ace shopper. She comes home with clothes that fit her and that she needs. She does not overspend. But when I move away for a while and enter stores alone, I come home with things that are the wrong color, size, and fit. I get caught up in the pitch and cannot wait to get home, so I say yes to everything she or he suggests, and then I come home to a pile of clothes that look and feel just terrible. Not that they are bad, but they are not me.

I do not like shopping in stores. I am just not equipped.

I hate how sales people look at and talk to me. I hate how I appear in the mirrors. I hate how I cannot ever stand up to a sales person. I hate being the center of his or her attention. I find a note I scribbled in a pocket of an old coat:

These Sales people make me feel pasty, ugly and unfashionable. Inferior.

Not the same way Harriet the Spy did. Because I admired Harriet. She has a skill set, good personality. She is deep, thoughtful, sensitive. These people just seem to want to be well groomed and sell. But I cannot stand up to them. I hate how I agree with them and wind up coming home with an outfit that is perfectly fine but unflattering on me. Or just not my style. I do not wear clothes to stay in style. Staying in style, in my opinion, is just desperate.

I tell all this to Mom (unedited, I would probably never be so honest and petty to anyone else, but Mom, I know, will always love me no matter what) who listens and then says she understands I am no trend whore, but as far as my negativity toward sales staff goes, I am being unkind, perhaps even self-serving. That it is easy, but wrong, to make up negative things about people, especially ones earning a paycheck. She says I am letting things get to me that I should not. And that my cynicism is not going to strengthen or better me. She says I am making those sales people out to be something they are not. They are just people, doing their job, following their training. She then goes on to say I have special taste, good taste. Maybe I know more than the sales people. Maybe I could educate them.

When my aunt Gina (Mom's sister – technically half sister – because of the same mom, different dad) comes home after living away for so many years and asks me if I would work in her new clothing store, Simply Separate, I think she is kidding. But as sometimes happens with wise relatives, she sees potential in me that I don't know I have.

Initially I question the value of that profession but grow to love it.

The love, the respect, takes a while.

So I, a lousy shopper (at least without Mom), carve out a profession working in retail. Initially I wonder *Is it enough? Will I still disappoint Dad?*

But progress is not linear, and that explains why I loved and still love dioramas: no trajectory.

The clothes at Simply Separate are carefully constructed. Better made than some of those enormous novels I read in bed on nights when Dino has Althea. I mean, I rely on big books – more than one gets me through an evening – but some just don't tell as good a story as our blue velvet, nipped-at-the waist biker midi jacket that sold out last fall. Or this season's black ruched skirt with an irregular hem and lace waist detail.

While I enjoy the store and my job, I cannot understand my aunt's faith in apparel, its power to protect, enhance, save, destroy. I respect but cannot entirely relate to her devotion.

I, unlike Mom, do not make accurate psychological portraits of individuals, so I am not going to say much more about Aunt Gina and her business skills and belief in contemporary attire now. I feel like I could say something, but it would smudge rather than clarify her complex, out-of-the-ordinary character. Maybe Mom will sketch her some day.

The thing, though, I will say about Aunt Gina is that she sticks by me.

This does not happen with everyone. This is an aside, but I have to put it somewhere, so why not here? My perspective on a pattern I must be more than partly to blame for, even though I do not entirely understand it: I meet countless people. First they think I am interesting and then they don't. Then, sometimes – but only sometimes – they do again. And usually when they do, it is after grasping my ties to charismatic people like Dino and Aunt Gina.

Aunt Gina is consistently popular, and she stands by me. Yes, probably because I am her niece but also, I hope, because she loves me and because she takes some delight that I am her offspring.

My basic take on her relationship to Simply Separate: Clothes are to my aunt what food is to Dino and Ily. What finance is to George. What stories are to Mom. I do not know if I will ever have an adult connection to or passion for a profession – or even hobby – like they do. This is what means the most to me:

relationships with human beings. My craving for people connections may be a pitfall. Or a strength. I was not always this
way. I think it started when I had Althea. Anyway, I deeply love
friends and family and really like the store.

Simply Separate rescues me. First, the name helps me finally
lose those hurt feelings left over from the conference Mom had
with that teacher who tells her I am simple, meaning dull and
ill-equipped.

Diorama assembly heals that some, but not completely.

Second, it teaches me to look differently at words: "Simple"
does not mean bad/stupid.

The store name, Simply Separate, comes from this line by a
great American poet, Walt Whitman:

One's-Self I sing, a simple separate person

(It is from a long poem, Leaves of Grass.)

To me, the line means being at once in and not in the stream
of things. Being In and Out.

Another thing the line makes me think: We – that is, people –
are and yet are not linked tightly together.

When you read more of Whitman's stanza, it also addresses
other things, like the social:

Yet utter the word Democratic, the word En-masse

The corporeal:

Of Physiology from top to toe I sing

Justice (because women could not vote when Whitman
wrote this):

The Female equally with the male I sing

Joy/zest:

Of Life immense in passion, pulse, and power

Contemporary:

The Modern Man I sing

I am no scholar, and neither is my aunt, but individuals, neighbors, bodies, and appetites are things she keeps in mind on buying trips.

By neighbors, we don't just mean people who live geographically close to one another.

Our bags (organic, beige) say this:

SIMPLY, SEPARATE

One's-Self I sing,
a simple separate
person*

*Walt Whitman

In between the store name and the quote and the author citation, there is a sketch of the great poet. A majestic presence: beard, high cheekbones, large-brimmed hat. When I see photographs of him, I am struck by his eyes. They are striking, and I have to stop myself from inventing stories about his personality (kind, mischievous, confident, passionate). But it is impossible for the drawing on Simply Separate packaging to capture all that.

In my opinion the line "Of Physiology from top to toe I sing" should be on the bags, but my aunt says people would think we were a juice bar or body-work studio.

The store boxes quote (well, reference, do not quote exactly) another great American, Gertrude Stein:

> **I dress for myself**
> **and**
> **strangers.**

(The original line: "I write for myself and strangers.")

By the way, if you ask me where "myself and strangers" leaves friends and family, I'd say, "Good question." Maybe in between one's self and strangers. Or overlapping.

Here is more of the quote, which is from *The Making of Americans*:

"I am writing for myself and strangers. This is the only way that I can do it. Everybody is a real one to me, everybody is like some one else too to me. No one of them that I know can want to know it and so I write for myself and strangers."

So both literary references that Gina chooses for her packaging contain the word "self," contain the word "of" in the work title, and are written by Americans. Though Simply Separate's designers are in fact global, she uses few American designers.

Aside: When Dino sees the store box, he says, "I cook for myself and for organs."

Over time, he stays attached to the slogan, but once he solidifies things with Ily, he changes the "I" to "we." They adopt the slogan, even have a plaque made:

WE COOK FOR OURSELVES AND FOR ORGANS.

They take it to each offal-specializing pop-up and hang it in their upstate establishment, when they finally get one.

Thinking about this makes me sad and happy at once. Sad because of what I lost. Happy because what we all have or are starting to maybe have.

Back to our boxes: Below Stein's quotation is a sticker of her. Whitman is sketched onto the bag. Stein's photograph is reproduced on a sticker and stuck on. The image is taken from an elegant photograph. She is relatively older, but she radiates well-being. So much is white: her hair, her blouse (wide collar, v-neck, closed with a broach).

The image of Gertrude Stein (solid, confident, relaxed) reminds me of a writer I met in person, Jim Harrison, a friend of Dad's whom I met in Florida. He stood under a palm tree, legs apart. He looked solid, rooted, and at ease. Gertrude and Jim both have broad faces. Both are beautiful. Not traditionally pretty or handsome but beautiful. Something inside radiates out. You just know these two are not socially awkward.

Social awkwardness. How do you know when you have it – or do others just notice and then talk about it? Is that, maybe, why people like me either at first or, in some cases, way later? Am I socially awkward, or do I just worry that I might be?

And, not to get ahead of my story, but just thinking here: My reluctance to value selling clothes is, maybe, what ultimately wrecks things with Dino.

He makes food, and I sell clothes. SHANKUS TWO's food and Simply Separate's clothes are nurturing, edgy, expressive. Yet I am not proud of this combination. At that time. If one person makes things, okay, then the other could be a doctor or investor or lawyer.

I cannot help but think of and deeply admire George and his strong balance sheet: booming bonds tied to green investments, heavy investments in infrastructure (roads, subway lines, bridges, hydroelectric dams), buildings (the one I live in), environmental bonds, and projects. It seems like you need at least one person like that in a couple. I mean, roads and buildings are valiant, so are things green. Worries about construction delays for a hydroelectric dam that will provide electricity for half of a country seems, to me, more worthy than lamb sushi or deciding whether to belt a tunic or let it hang loose.

Just like I do not feel clothes are enough, I do not feel like food is enough. This belittles Dino's calling, his passion. I mean, you could also say it belittles me, but that is another story. The point here is Dino and why things work out with Ily. I see this now, that he is with Ily. Food is everything to them both. Couples often work so much better when there is a shared passion.

The world needs participation, like Dad says.

Socially conscious entrepreneurship makes connections between things. If I cannot do that, it would be good if, at least, I was hitched with someone who could. Not saying George, but maybe a man with some of his qualities.

As an adult, I still hold tight to dreams (stories). Sometimes, that strategy serves me. Other times, it does not – like when I am convinced Dino wants to come back to me.

What is the difference between believing stories and being delusional?

For example, the time when I start to believe that Dino will send me the YouTube link to the G Love and Special Sauce's song "Just Fine." The singer repents a dalliance, ("and I don't love her half as much as this guitar that I'm playin'") but wants and hopes to get back together with the lover he cheated on. ("Let's try this one more time again / I want your name on my rhyme again / We'll be just fine...") That, to me, is our song, mine and Dino's. I believe we are in step and believe he senses so, too. I picture him finding the link to the song and texting it to me. Or sending the CD to our apartment, wrapped in bright paper, maybe with a bouquet of flowers. Roses. White roses. A large bouquet, more than a dozen. Maybe thirty, forty, white roses. Maybe he includes champagne. Or airline tickets, maybe to Tokyo, a city he loves but never visits with me.

Truth is, I'd be happy with a simple text of the link. Maybe with a note ("Love You Babe"). This makes me think of the next song he could send, once we get back together and are settled into a rhythm, "I Got You Babe."

This story gets me through an afternoon. Simply Separate is busy. At the end of my shift, I look forward to his message. I have several, but none from Dino. I smile. Maybe this is because he is going to surprise me on the street or better yet at home. Maybe he gets his twin brother, George, to watch Althea for a bit, enough time for us to share a romantic interlude. It has been a while. I feel thankful I've kept my daily dose of pineapple juice. Before walking to Althea's after-school program, I slip on my pepper-spray bracelet and change into higher heeled boots than I usually wear when I walk in the city. But not too high. I don't want to look desperate, and above all I don't want to look like a fashion victim, but these give my legs a lift. I walk different, feel different, in heels. I hold in my stomach and grip my buttocks – thank you, hula hooping – to keep a regular walking pace and feel like a woman. I know this sounds silly, but it is true.

I walk down the street, check my phone regularly. Well, maybe a lot. But a lot compared to what? I just am not sure since I see people (not that I snoop, though it might sound like it) bend over phones in the library and on the subway and at the grocery store. Maybe they are reading poems, political articles, or looking up meal suggestions or ten-minute workouts. But maybe they, like me, are hoping for, banking on, a message from a certain someone. Anyway, I bend over my own phone and skim weather forecasts and friendly and business notes. I delete spam, wanting only Dino's specific message regarding that one song and proclaiming what he feels but cannot express. I long, am fired up for, his ping. Maybe it will come when I stand in line with Althea at the frozen yogurt shop after I pick her up. Maybe I show it to her. Maybe we tap our feet together, listen to, sing along with it. Then he shows up at our apartment with a guitar, singing the song or the most important bars from it. Picture us all laughing because, though Dino sings, he sings badly. Though he plays the guitar, again, it is badly. Even though he has been taking lessons from our neighbor, a concert cellist, Bruce. But his bad playing doesn't matter because he sings and plays with heart, humor. I picture our musical encounter in such detail. I start to think it has already happened, that we are over our hump. That he is home, now, making an appetizer. I approach the school, humming. Smile at the staff. Althea, in a good mood, puts down her finger stitching, hugs me, and reminds me her dad and uncle are taking her out to dinner tonight.

We walk home. On the way, we pass Bruce, dressed in his tux, lugging his cello to work. He waves, tousles Althea's hair, kisses my cheek, tells us he found a terrific chiropractor for his chronic back pain and that he plans to stop into Simply Separate tomorrow to get his mom a birthday gift. See why I love our neighborhood? The brief interactions. They seem like nothing but over time add up to everything.

Althea and I get home. No one is there.

She opens her backpack and starts on schoolwork while I empty the dishwasher. The bell rings.

"Here," says Dino to the intercom. Actually his "Here" sounds more like a bark. I feel sadness in my stomach.

I buzz him in, along with his twin, George. Althea leaps into her dad's arms, wraps her legs around his waist, nuzzles his neck. They stay like that for a while. I look at George, whisper that he should ask Althea to take him to her room and play her banjo. "In a minute," he says, watching the father-daughter scene.

When Althea and Dino untwine, George says, "Hey, favorite niece." (Ja better never hear him talk like this.) "Play me some banjo."

Me and Dino, alone.

I tilt my head, smile, say, "You've got my name on your rhyme again."

"What?"

"G Love. That line from our song, 'You've got my name on your rhyme again.'"

"Who?"

"G Love. And Special Sauce. That song, our song, 'Just Fine'"

"Meg, you don't have to be sarcastic."

"Dino, no, I mean, I am sorry. Sorry. Don't you remember how I loved that G Love song?"

"Who?"

"Honey, I am not sarcastic. Just hopeful."

"Meg, you are just fucking all over the place."

"Honey – "

"Please stop talking to me this way."

"What?"

"You've gotta move on."

"Dino, how can you say that?"

"Meg, you know this is right. Use that spine of yours," he says, turning away, not touching me anywhere. Not my neck, head, cheek, even shoulder. Walking into Althea's room, he shouts, "Who is hungry besides me?"

There is one strong example of story delusion.

But, honestly, I believed and did not believe at the same time. I believed it could happen, yet completely understood it would not.

Who cares? I would rather spend the day believing (the preparation, the heels, the humming, the message checks, the dreams of reunion pleasure) than not. I would rather devote a day to imagining all that than sloshing around in a gray zone or envisioning the worst. This way, I extended our relationship. We gain an extra day, though not an evening. But I look back on the day, my faith, its arrangements, and its potential fondly.

Back to me and Ily.

She better not fucking touch my daughter! And better not try to do that relationship thing where the step-mom plays good cop and spoils her and then I have to come down hard.

I feel bad for saying that. Stepmothers can be good for children.

Sometimes, I see sense only after over reacting. Only then do I see the over reaction is irrational, not good.

Also, George says he doesn't think Ily really likes kids. I hope this is true.

See? What kind of person am I? Who would want her daughter around someone who doesn't want them to be around? Honestly? Me. Because then I won't have to share her with anyone. This is immature, and I am ashamed. Mom would for sure be ashamed.

Ily and I are not classic beauties.

I probably put more effort into fashion and being appealing than she does, but I don't think in the obvious ways, and I don't know that I look better.

Ily is sturdy with her short legs and thick neck. She, like me, has curves and sizable hips and would have no problem giving birth. In a way, I wish she was luminous, otherworldly, because then I could say Dino went for something opposite of me or even superficial. But she is a regular, hard working woman who is confident and attractive, not vain. She wears her hair in a ponytail or bun. She dresses badly – no, wrong word, dresses for comfort is a better description. I mean, when not wearing her cook's pants and jacket with Crocs, she wears orthopedic clogs and loose dresses with patterns (floral, stripes, gingham) that come below her knees. She has naturally rosy cheeks and thick dark eyebrows. White teeth. She is an avid swimmer. Also runs and lifts weights. She, used to lifting heavy pans, has strong arms.

Her hands have burn marks from grease splatter and careless hot pan handling. Objectively speaking, I would say she is pretty from the inside and radiates a warmth and confidence. So those are some things about Ily.

One more thing: She, like Dino, is a shark. Meaning goal-oriented. Nothing gets in their way. I have been described as flakey and all over the place. It is true. I can see how that irritates someone like Dino, with his bulldozer tendencies.

When I settle down and consider everything, I come to this: Dino falls in love with Ily because of who she is. Flaws and all. This is, to me, the kicker. I can never be flawed around Dino and always feel I have to be perfect for him. Dress well, have sweet breath, taste good, be kind, gentle, a good listener. Hide my inadequacies, even improve or eradicate them. How great it must be for Ily to be around Dino and let her deficiencies hang out. When I think this way, I start feeling steamed. Why? Because of Ily. Who has things so easy. Who seems to have so much luck. Who gets my husband and not even because she is perfect.

This is an unproductive line of thought.

But I am not ready to leave it.

And here is another thing: I am learning, now that I have been abandoned by my husband and am meeting other abandoned women.

Before I go on, let me just say I understand that men are left by women, too. I am not leaving those guys out. It is just not a situation I am intimate with. So, yes, it happens. I am not ignorant of that, but no I will not address that here. But might later.

Sometimes, we are left for someone younger, exotic, impeccable, a true beauty. I think this is most of the times, not sometimes, until I land in this position. Then learn about times a wife is not left for a woman more powerful and beautiful but for one who is hard up, troubled, needy. I mean, these are stories I overhear in the coffee shops and on the playground. Sometimes, men want to be with a woman they can help, or try to help, rather than someone pretty, passionate, and powerful.

Not that I am any of those things compared with Ily. But even if I were, it might make me feel better about myself, though really it does not. Because what good does it do to be prettier and healthier than the person you are left for? (Not that I am, by the way, prettier or healthier or more successful than Ily.) I'm just asking what if. What good would it do if I were?

I shelve my stories temporarily. Understand this might be part of what Dad means by participate.

I realistically consider this:

Dino. He needs to be the kind of chef he wants to be and cook for the kinds of people he wants to cook for. When he finds that is not happening in our neighborhood, which I love and make us move to, I ignore him. Tell him to make his restaurant, SHANKUS TWO, work. Would not even consider moving to a location that might make his business more successful.

Two, I am not sure our combined skill set makes for long-term, powerful coupling.

Three, I love this city. Maybe more than Dino. Or at least my structure of living here. I love being married with Dino in the city, but would I love being married to him outside of it?

This sounds so corny, but, hey, I Love This City. Its streets, people, buildings, river, coffee. Their clothes. My neighbors. (Hi, Bruce!) The different paces that people – cops, doctors, construction crews, waiters, actors – take to work and appointments. (Bolting paces and steady, meandering ones.) Interesting but sensible shoes, jackets, dresses. All-Weather preparation: umbrella, rain boots, protective hats. The restaurants, venting food fragrances out on the sidewalks. The organ music played in churches you can hear walking by on Sunday mornings or during evening choir practices. The tourists. The ones who proudly acknowledge their home states: "I Heart Michigan," "Floridians Do It Better," "BRAZIL." The ones who dress impractically, sometimes in heels, and have to remove them, walking barefoot until they come to a place that sells flip flops, disposable Mary-Jane flats, or the pricier European comfort sandals. The ones who complain about the dirt, the pace, hotel-room sizes and prices. The ones whose eyes are glazed with joy and amazement.

I love movies, see as many as I can, and am not saying this to take a thing away from going to the cinema – but watching people on these streets can be, for me, almost as interesting.

Four, when I think of my in-laws and their solid marriage (I am not idealizing – those two are happy) I realize they build SHANKUS together, then work there, together. SHANKUS is theirs. SHANKUS TWO does not belong to Dino and me, really. It belongs to Dino. I do not work there, and if I visit, it is to talk, eat, or drink usually with George and/or Althea. Or to bring him clean running shorts and socks.

Five, full disclosure: I never carried pepper spray as a child and do not carry it now. I do not have a bracelet containing it in my wardrobe, though I like the idea and think that maybe it is something to propose to Aunt Gina, something to manufacture for Simply Separate? Maybe a ring is a better container, an aerosol ring, bulky, for the thumb or middle finger. Or possibly a pendant? I do sometimes pretend to carry it. Not because I have ever needed to use it for defense but because the fantasy provides me with invisible armor and courage and reminds me to walk, sit, stand with stomach engaged, spine straight, forehead smooth and at least not furrowed.

Six, I am attracted to the idea of men more interested in business than their craft. That is not Dino.

Seven, I want Dino to love me, maybe even more than I love him. I want to be the woman of his dreams, which is egocentric and just plain wrong. It is about control and not love. I want to win, so spend all this time trying to be something I am not rather than settling into my flaws, fortune, visual acuity, and sweet, smoky vagina.

Meg and Emily

We are Family
Nile Rodgers and Bernard Edwards

Our friend Bry, a writer, who thinks everyone should read and most should at least try to write, runs a nice reading series in our shop. When she understands I am absolutely not going to write, she asks me if I might read some of Mom's stuff. This seems alarmingly personal to me. Everything I've ever read by Mom seems to be directed to me or about me in the most embarrassingly personal ways, ways that might not be obvious to anyone else. When I try to explain this to her, she says she understands completely but that literature is bigger than people. She says I should think about it.

I love Bry.

But am bound to disappoint her.

Mom wrote some pieces about the Shankus family – one of which deals with inventing things to do with their ancestry. Here is a piece Mom wrote that she wants me to read. I tell Mom this should not be read in public, that it might offend the Shankus family. She says not to be silly, that it is vaguely connected to my in-laws, sister-in-law, and ex-husband. I say okay, but I still think it is better left unread. Unless it is read out loud in public, not by me. Bruce, our neighbor the cellist, does it.

– III –

Three Portraits – For The Shankus Family
Not Strictly True History
By Emily Kitto

THORA SHAMBES
I was born in Sparta, a land-locked region of Greece. My mother, father and three older sisters lived in one house. Next door, on one side, my maternal grandparents. On the other side, our aunt, uncle, and six cousins. My grandmother (yaya) had tiny, deep-set eyes. I remember her sitting inside, staring out the window. Staying inside then, during the day, was odd. Everyone thought so. Our homes in Sparta were not like homes are now. They were small, and the floors were dirt. We did most things (cooking, working, eating, sometimes even sleeping) outside. My mother said her mother was not always like that – that is, sitting

indoors, staring. But around the time my oldest sister, Georgia, was born, our yaya, my mom told us, changed. She stopped sweeping the floor and washing clothes and bedding the way she used to. She cooked only the simplest foods (rice, tea, broth) rather than the pleasurable, carefully spiced, meals (lamb, goat, soup, custard) she used to fix over the pit in her backyard. She used to garden and take long walks, our mom said. But all I remember is yaya sitting alone, staring out the window, not talking, except to explain her condition. Her reasoning: She sensed very bad things coming. And this suspicion pulled her away from her life, from family, friends, and work. Pulled her into a gloomy world of waiting for terrible things to come. And come they did. Because of the awful things that came, I was forced to leave her, my entire family, and our house in Sparta. I had to make a new life, apart from all that, in the U.S.A.

I have a beautiful family here. If I had stayed in Greece, I would never have met my husband, Bill, or had our five daughters. I am blessed to be in the U.S.A with Bill and our girls. We have a good house that sits on a small hill on Hamilton Street. We can walk to church and the girls' school. But I have trouble. One problem is that I cannot bring my two families and two countries side-by-side. They are separate when they should be together. I miss everything about Sparta. The bigger problem has to do with the reason I had to leave. The reason is so terrible. I have a hard time thinking about it. I can't always control when

I do and when I do not. It's getting to the point, to be truthful, when I barely ever can control it. The story of why I left Sparta trickles, oozes, even floods into my thinking whenever it wants. It didn't used to be this way. I used to be able to block it out, and then sometimes, late at night in the safe arms of Bill or rocking one of our daughters, when I felt loved, protected, I could think about it just in bits. But now it is different. The story forces its way in whenever it wants – like when I hand out baklava after church or make meatballs in our kitchen or fold laundry in our basement. All I can do is give into it. Say, "Okay. You win." The story comes so hard and so fast, I have no armor, no protection. I find I must sit down wherever I am and cry. It takes me over. If it happens inside our home, it's not so bad. My family is used to seeing me cry. But last week it happened in our front yard when I was picking dandelion greens. There, on our front lawn in our subdivision, where any neighbor or passerby could see. It has not yet happened at church or in the grocery store. I'm so afraid it will. I sense yaya hovering over me, whispering, "See? See? See, Thora? I was not a crazy old lady who lost her mind like everyone said. I was right, right, right!" I hear her voice like a strong hiss. I see her tiny eyes. Now they look wise to me when they used to seem scary, crazy. Now I understand she was not nuts. She was right.

It hurts me to write this. It hurts my head, my eyes, my shoulders. My stomach, knees, ankles. I know I can't say in detail what frightened yaya, what she saw coming, what turned out to be true, what sent me away from Greece. If I do, it will beat me up. Isn't the important thing that my yaya sensed bad things coming and they did?

BILL SHANKUS

I was born in the Peloponnese, Greece. I am a tiny, thin man. Dark complexion. But I am strong. I fought in WWI. So did my older brother. After the war, he met and married a French girl. I came back to Greece. I am the second oldest of eight children. Then, there, with that many children, people do not notice so much if one moves here or there. So when my brother moved to France, I decided to take a boat to the U.S.A. We had an uncle there, in New York. I was on the boat twice as long as I should have been. The reason might make me seem naïve or stupid. Maybe neither or both are true. But I met a nice fellow, Geoff, on the boat. I thought he was nice. He did not have the money he needed to get off the boat but told me that his wife, waiting for him, was pregnant. That he had three other children. That his family, without him, was poor and starving. That he needed the money to get off the boat so he could meet them, start working, start earning money. Otherwise they would all end up in a place like a jail. Geoff told me that the U.S.A was like that. If people cannot earn money, they got locked up. I thought about this and felt bad for him. I had met guys in the war who were tormented and who could not take care of their families. They worried about their wives and kids. Geoff made me think of them. I decided he needed to disembark more than I did. That I could arrange to work on the boat back to Greece, then again on its way to the U.S.A, and earn enough to disembark plus more. This might sound foolish, now, but it turned out to be the best decision I ever made because if I had not made it, I would have disembarked then and stayed in New York to meet my uncle. But what happened was this: On the second boat ride, my uncle and I met a cousin. He was heading to meet relatives in Flint, Michigan. He said there were more opportunities there, in the Midwest, for Greeks. So when I got to the USA and finally disembarked in New York City, my uncle and cousin and I made our way to Flint, Michigan. There I met Thora, the love of my life. As I have said, I am a small, thin, dark man. Thora is pale, blond-haired, blue-eyed (people from Sparta have this coloring) and curvy. Her cheeks, her breasts, her waist, her thighs – they are all soft, curvy. I was thin, wiry. We looked totally opposite. I guess in some way we were. But we fell in love right away. Then had the five girls. That was hard on Thora, taking care of those girls. Each one smart, beautiful, mouthy, independent. They fought, laughed, sang, screamed, and brought home boys. Not always Greek. Each one went to college and got a teaching certificate. I made sure of that. I did not want them to depend on any man who might have to leave them to fight in a war or lose his job. I wanted them to have their own security. After years working in restaurants, I opened my own, The Honeydell. We had standard Greek food but also special chocolates. I loved the April Fools' Day in the U.S.A. It struck me as such a funny idea. At the Honeydell, for April Fools', we dipped garlic in chocolate and gave it to the customers. You've never seen such looks on people's faces. After a while, our regulars knew and would not bite, but they brought unsuspecting friends and guests. After a longer while, everyone knew, and it was not worth continuing the tradition.

ALTHEA SHAMBES (mother of Thora)

My life started with beauty, love, and promise before it turned rotten. Not every single thing went rotten, but enough terrible things happened to wreck my heart. I never will understand why God – who I love, do not get me wrong – brought what he did to our family. I try to focus on the good points: my love for the remaining daughters; my husband, Nick; our family and neighbors. Sometimes, I blame my mother. She said she saw bad things coming. But I wonder if her conviction bad things were coming produced them? I understand that, sometimes, people believe expecting the worst prepares them for if and when bad times ever come. I used to believe that. My mother drilled it into me. But now I am not so sure. Now I wonder if believing bad things will happen makes them happen.

My husband, Nick, and I – both born and raised in Sparta, Greece – had four beautiful daughters. When I say they were beautiful, I am not bragging. Beauty is beauty. What can you do with it? Who is responsible? No one. Brains, kindness, work ethic – these can be taught. But beauty just pops out. By any standards, our girls were beautiful. One day, our oldest, Georgia, did not come home. Georgia was a good, good girl. Being the oldest sister, she was reliable. Something was wrong. Wrong, wrong, wrong. Days went by, and we could not find her. Some people suggested she ran away with a boy. But we, her family, knew her too well. After three days, another girl went missing. This girl was the same age as Georgia and even prettier. Then a few days later, another girl. So everyone in our village who had daughters kept them close to home. We didn't let them out of our sight. Keeping our girls nearby was almost as bad as worrying about the missing girls. At that time, in our village, everyone wandered around all of the time. We lived, worked, and socialized outside. Our home had a dirt floor. We barely spent time there. So detaining our daughters was awful. If I sound cold, listing facts and so little emotion, it is only because that is the only way I can tell it. There is no other way. I cannot describe the fear, the nightmares, the pain, the sadness. The hate. I just cannot. No words fit with what we felt, what we went through. They simply do not. And my mother, with her small eyes, saying this is what she expected, all along. This situation – these missing girls – this is why she stopped cleaning, talking, going to church, changing her clothes, doing much cooking, and just spending her time staring out a window. Sometimes drooling. Often stinking. This, these missing girls, she saw it coming. After a few months, no more girls disappeared. But none ever came back. There is a possible story here. A detective who comes to solve this crime, who finds the missing beautiful girls, or who learns what happened to them. Learns who is responsible. That would be such a good story. This is not that story. I wish it was.

Our account is bad, ugly. We lost one daughter and lived with our three other daughters, but nothing seemed the same. Nothing seemed safe. When our cousins from the U.S.A. came to visit, my husband, Nick, and I both had the same idea to have them take one of our daughters with them. The U.S.A. might not be safe, but neither was our village. And our daughter might reach a dream. Get rich. Have a family. Come back and take care of us. When our cousins Pauline and Frank came, we asked them. Long story short, they agreed. They asked if it could be Thora. They love all their nieces, but she was the youngest and might have the best chance to adapt, grow, shine. So we lost our little girl. Over the years, we wrote to her. We sent her olives, lemons, and wine. We hoped she would ask us to visit her in the U.S.A. – or at least visit us with her husband, the restaurant owner, Bill, and their five girls. But she never did. She wrote to me she could not bear it. To see us again. That it would eat her like acid. When she said this, I worried she was like my mother, her yaya. That she had that dark tendency. And I did not want her husband and family in the U.S.A. to be brought down by that darkness, to have to meet with any of that bad fire. The insane kind that breeds awful. I kept thinking how we lost my mother to her worries about things to come. I did not want Thora's family to lose her because of things that came. I wrote to her that we are too busy to visit and that we understand why she will not come back. I say this again and again: "We will always love you." And so on. I hope my permission will lighten, maybe protect her. Help her appreciate and nourish her family without getting caught up and broken by our past.

In the end, we lost two daughters but only have a story for one. None of the families learned about the girls. We try to talk to one another. We go between having conversations that are too close and that get uncomfortable to seeking complete avoidance. We know too much. I still think there might be a good story for Thora. She did find love and wealth, even given those letters about her darkness. I pray she can find and hold onto some happiness in that big and way-off U.S.A.

– END –

Aunt Gina serves retsina. Bruce does a Great Job. Everyone in the store laughs, hugs, cries, especially the Shankus family. Panna tells Mom that she is complimented by the entertaining, inventive tales.

"Not us but so us," she says.

Emily Kitto

My level-headedness does not always last, but it helps me move on. I have to thank Mom. Here is another one of her inventions with healing properties:

> For Meg,
> This is For You. It is Not You.
> Entirely.
> It might suggest
> a new way to look at things.
> Remember that nipped
> at the waist velvet biker jacket
> you and Aunt Gina sold? It referenced
> motorcycles along with things Victorian?

Remember how you turned
that digit, 7, into a ballerina?
Remember that portrait of Dad with
the elongated nose? It was not
Dad's nose but somehow it captured
something of him. That is what I
try to do here. Plus it gave me
a chance to re-read Anna Karenina. I am not telling
you what to do – it never works – but it
would not harm you to read the great
novel. I agree
with Bry, reading is good for everyone.
But Meg, darling, you have a good
imagination. Use it to pull out of
any funk you get dragged into.
And consider what love is, really.
And what it is not. Love You,
Mom

– IV –

Tap Tap Tap
By Emily Kitto

I cannot say *Anna Karenina* is my favorite book, but it is one I pick up and flip through often for the descriptions of cold winters, rich food, riding boots, puffing engines, chirping birds.

Turkish towels. Tea, gazebos, fields, satin dresses, trembling train platforms. Anna's different red bags and purses.

And lines like this one from Anna: "I so wish you would all love me as I love you."

And descriptions of Vronsky losing touch after he falls in love with Anna, perceiving people as objects: beds, trees, lampposts.

But I also return to this book for its irritating opening sentence:

"All happy families are alike; each unhappy family is unhappy in its own way."

Irritating because that sentence is filled with the importance of truth while it is and is not true.

Can you follow the logic and say, "All happy people are alike, each unhappy person is unhappy in his or her own way"?

Happy People.

Not self-realized people who, like Job, survive and even grow from loss, punishment, and degradation.

But like men and women who effortlessly enjoy good fortune. Who have a spring in their step. People who whistle in the shower and who are liked by neighbors, children, spouses, strangers, and co-workers. People who make new friends but keep the old. Can you say those people are all alike?

I hope for happiness and even try to have faith it exists, but I believe it is unhappiness that ignites existence or, in any case, breeds stories. If I know one thing, it is this: People need stories, even the ones who say they do not.

Some look to literature for their stories, but even those who do not – even those who read for detail, rhythm, visuals, and reshuffled tropes – are plot dependent. What is gossip but a series of stories? What are politics, what is religion, what is self-esteem? What, in fact, is love?

Everything I have just said is grossly simplified and arguably untrue. Still, I have spent so much of my medium-length, medium-quality life not saying things because I think of all the exceptions and all the points that could contradict, even detonate, my own, so I now try to do something different with my broad, if arrogant, inaccurate, statements. Maybe it does not work. Maybe it will never work, me stating something reeking of truth. Generalization, pushing something forth, brings on anxiety. Yet I remind myself that sweeping statements did not worry Tolstoy, so maybe I should try not to let them worry me.

Here is a truth: I recently learned my husband is having an affair.

My first response – rather than asking him who or why or saying that I am crushed or even just breaking down and crying – is to tell him he must move out of our house at once. I hope he will say, "NO!" or "PLEASE LET ME STAY!" I wish to hear him haltingly describe the love – cavernous, frightening – he has for me. To hear him admit that he is self-destructive, deeply so, and to tell me I must understand his affair under the umbrella of that self-destruction. I hope he will say that behavior that seems cruel and coarse is a frightened shout for love. Or at least I hope he will tell me he screwed up, perhaps because of a mid-life crisis.

But rather than do any of those things he becomes stone cold. All that comes out of his mouth are concerns about property and statements that completely miss the point. He says things like, "Listen. I never did anything with her inside our apartment – or even the restaurant."

This all takes place just when we move out of our apartment, temporarily, during extensive renovation to make two medium-sized apartments into one large one. The plan is to stay at my aunt's, who is abroad indefinitely. Her apartment is just a few blocks from ours and our restaurant. Or maybe now I should say, "The restaurant."

When I learn about Dino's affair, I send our daughter, Althea, to Dino's sister, Ja. My sister-in-law does not take her brother's side. His twin brother, George, does not either. I stay at my aunt's, hoping Dino will visit. It is where I am now.

What a picture: me, sprawled on a leather lounge chair in my aunt's complexly decorated dressing room. There is a large mirror in front of me. When I look in it, I appear to be resting, but I am not resting. I am distraught, agitated, spinning out of control. I look away from the mirror to the wall facing the street. It has a large window covered by heavy, closed drapes. A narrow ribbon of light breaks through a small gap between the two bunches of material. I do not want to open up the drapes and let all that is outside in. I am just barely able to handle looking at the little light strip.

My aunt's apartment is never boring. It features rich, complex collections of chairs, sofas, carpets, tables, and paintings. She encourages me to wear anything in her wardrobe, an instructive exercise in restrained chic. I learn so much from examining, trying on, and wearing her high-necked coats, sleeveless ribbed tunics with uneven hems, leggings, lace tops, capes, ballet flats, shoe boots.

Now, I am in one of her dressing gowns, a deep-pocketed, silky, leopard-patterned wrap that hits just below my knees. On my feet are her embroidered mule slippers, which are velvet, black, and covered in tiny gold tulips. This attire gives me a feeling of living some grand, impressive, life that is definitely not mine. I fall asleep, looking at the wall, the drapes, the thin strip of light. I dream this:

Dinner, in a castle, overlooking a sparkling lake in a mountainous European country. Twenty guests occupy a long, wide, glass-legged, glass-topped table. The table is so wide that it is impossible to converse across it. Little microphones are set at each place setting. Next to each microphone is a number "One" through "Twenty." If you want to speak to a guest, you press his or her assigned number.

A vague, bloated figure presides over the dinner, but it is never clear who this is or where he or she is positioned.

Communication goes smoothly. "Thirteen" pushes "Seven." "Twelve" pushes "One." Now, recounting the dream, I picture potential interference problems. What if more than one person or even every person wants to speak with "Thirteen"? This does not happen in my dream. Maybe this is the same thing as other things that do not happen in dreams: drinking, cooking, kissing, eating, instrument playing.

The dinner is packed with tall handsome men who are apparently interested in me. I decide to enjoy the attention and not to worry, to be skeptical, or to question their sincerity.

A series of platters line the table's center full of oysters, duck, asparagus, pomegranates, champagne, whipped cream. No one eats or drinks. It all stays put as one sexy and varied still life.

A band plays. Guests dance. I wear a billowy blue chiffon floor-length dress with a wide sash, a dress unlike anything owned by me or my aunt. She favors and has taught me to favor straight, form-fitting dresses in blacks, browns, and maroons. My hair is piled up high on my head. I wear heavily jeweled dangly earrings and am concerned that their weight might over stretch out my pierced ear lobes. One of the taller men takes my hand, leads me onto the dance floor. We move, and his hands grip my waist. "Inside decoration, inside decoration," he whispers in my ear. "Inside, inside, inside decoration."

Guests at the table tap their glasses with forks and knives, signaling we should kiss. Just as our lips touch, the tapping grows unbearably loud. Tap tap tap. Tap tap tap. Tap tap tap. The elegant ballroom becomes a drafty school lunch hall.

Tap tap tap: The lunch-hall patrol raps on the table, tells us to stop food fighting.

Tap tap tap, tap tap tap.

My eyes open to the sliver of sun shining through my aunt's heavily brocaded drapes. I regret waking up. My dream, even the part in the school lunch hall, is much nicer than this real world.

I finger the cigarette lighter in the robe's pocket, wish I smoked, and think, *Why can't I start?*

Tap tap tap.

Someone knocks.

My husband! I jump up, tell myself to slow down. I pinch my cheeks. Breathe. Tighten the belt, loosen the neck of the dressing gown. Glide to the door. I stand there, hand on the knob, pull in my stomach, push out my chest. I open the door.

It is not my husband. It is my aunt's partner, Kitty, who has long blond hair, a creamy fleece shawl, a silver tunic, and slim dark pants. She asks if I plan to move over to the bed she turned down for me in the bedroom or to stay here in this dressing room on the lounging chair. Also, am I hungry because she is making a beet and carrot soup?

Here is what I honestly feel to be true but hope to be false: My husband loves me but is not in love with me and is relieved to now have to end our marriage. Somewhere deep in my gut

I understand this. Understand that it is futile to hope for and to fantasize about him coming here to confess great love, beg for forgiveness, admit shame and guilt – but my thoughts still scamper in that direction. I, overcome with heavy helplessness, stand and stare at Kitty, not answering her questions about rooms and food. She kisses my forehead and hands me a glass of sherry and a ceramic plate with a beautifully cut, fanned-out pear. She says, "Drink. Nibble. I am going to finish the soup."

I take the plate and the glass and return to the lounge chair. I see myself in that mirror as a disheveled woman who is worn out, perhaps from living for so long in denial.

I turn away from the mirror to the other wall, the one opposite the drapery. There are several bookcases. I take a sip of sherry, walk over to them. On top of the case is a Bible. I open it to this passage: "If a man is lazy, the rafters sag; if his hands are idle, the house leaks."

I know this phrase, heard it paraphrased as "Idle hands are the devil's work tool."

I am troubled by such infatuation with busyness. Does work make you free? If you spend all of your time being busy, then when do you have time to reflect, contemplate, imagine, sort out?

Still, there is something to be said for productivity to lift one out of moping, brooding periods of self-disgust.

I stare at my aunt's other books, which include novels, fairy tales, and histories, including a volume about Henry the VIII and his six wives.

A small pile of blank notebooks sits next to it. I pick one up. Inside its front cover is a pen. Without thinking too hard, I start scribbling, making up a story about Dino and his woman, his new woman – who happens, like him, to be a chef, a gifted chef. I decide my portrait will make her out to be fantastic, witchy, wily, spellbinding. I will model her after Henry VIII's second wife, Anne Boleyn, who had a tiny waist, delicate skin, sharp teeth, and a six-fingered left hand. No one can blame a man – a king like Henry or a simple chef like my Dino – seduced by an enchantress. The seduction just cannot be seen, in that case, as their responsibility.

– END –

Ily Shankus

Oh I'm on my way I know I am
Cat Stevens

Great Grandma's presence, which is familiar, non judgmental, provides me with solid listenership. Soon, though, I sense she wants me to move forward, erect something risky on that foundation. I also sense that she grows increasingly uncomfortable with my topics and personal choices.

I figure out ways to direct my thoughts to a broader group and picture several people (some familiar, others imagined) in a room (comfortable chairs, drinks, snacks). We talk. Sometimes one on one and sometimes as a whole bunch.

What follows is my communicating, in my head, with them.

I meet and completely fall for Dino. Sense in my gut we will be together some day, but after six intense weeks, not *at the time.* Sounds like a bogus break up line, "We are not good for each other, *at the time.*"

But it is true.

We *were* not.

But *are*.

I sleep with him immediately, bypassing Mom's advice about playing hard to get once I meet The One. *At the time,* I suspect he uses me. Guys like Dino – eighteen, handsome, cocky, talented – use women. Sometimes. Especially unworldly, shabbily dressed ones like me. I am very pretty, just not sophisticated, stylish, or elusive. Handsome young men, in my experience, go for chic dressers who throw out a challenge.

By the way, referring to myself as *very pretty* is not a boast. I cannot take credit for being born this way.

I can, and do, take credit for working hard on my swim speeds, summer soups, and beekeeping.

To be clear, I do not judge the fashion-conscious. It is just personally not a priority for me. If I sound defensive, it is not because I have a problem with fashion but because there are periods in my life when I feel pressure to take style more seriously than I want to.

Here is a letter – embarrassing, unsent – that I start to my oldest friend about Dino. I keep it all these years because it expresses a part of me I hope to leave but never forget.

Dear Betsy,

I met a guy who is EVERYTHING. Too EVERYTHING. I am not ready. Have a feeling it will lead to something if I wait. Being so far from home makes me feel stupid. Betsy, I need to grow. His name is Dino. I do not even want to spend any more time describing him to you because I am afraid I will jinx our chance for a forever future.

Betsy is an important part of my juvenile history. So are these foods:

Oven Baked (if no access to a campfire) Marshmallows

Dough Boys (best straight from the heat, eaten off the stick – but wait till they cool down)

Red Pop (toxic dye, great taste)

Olive Burgers (with *Miracle Whip,* not *Hellman's*)

Popcorn Balls (be careful with, or avoid, if wearing braces)

Aerosol Cheese (rarely – but wow)

Wacky Cupcakes, dotted with green frosting circles and red sprinkles (my first recipe – it becomes an annual staple at Apples & Eats)

These are not foods I grow up eating often. I share them with friends and family on special occasions. I remember drinking Red Pop only once, and it was at a cook out. Remember spraying the cheese twice, both times at school dances. The Wacky Cupcakes were, still are, part of our city's annual fall festival.

Another reason I keep that letter and the food list is to remind myself it is *okay* to behave and eat like a dope. If you never allow yourself that, you stop growing. Intelligence, sophisticated palettes, articulate sentences – they all have their place, but in excess they function as armor. You've got to let that go, periodically, or else it squeezes you in, squashes you down. Allowing those moments to savor junk and to sound ill informed is an experimental, risky gesture, a move that possibly paves roads to growth and expansion.

I take Dino's name, Shankus, long before we reunite, making me no longer Ily McGee but Ily Shankus. This might sound creepy, but it is for a strictly practical reason, which I will explain soon.

We are together, now, all these years later.

Patience has its rewards.

For my first waitress job, I work a diner counter. A customer – female, middle-aged, solid frame (a swimmer, I guess) – enters and orders coffee and an omelette. For some reason, it takes our kitchen forever. I refill her cup, apologize for the delay.

"No problem," she says, sipping her coffee, crossing her legs, looking around the diner in a pleasant, interested way.

My boss, watching her, says, "Patience is sexy. Why doesn't anyone ever fucking tell you *that*?"

I didn't think about it then, but, boy, do I think about it now.

Patience *is* sexy.

Anyway, *at the time,* I do not want to give Dino my heart just to get it smashed.

So after a hot start, we cool down.

Dino moves onto Ceil, unsurprisingly, the best cook in our class, the prettiest, too.

I hook up with Ted, who I meet at the pool. I look forward to the expression on Dino's face when he sees us together. Ted is much taller than Dino. I do not value height, but Dino is sensitive about being on the short side.

I want to love Ted way more than I do and sense he feels the same about me. Sometimes, people fall helplessly in love, and other times we *really try* to make magic happen.

I raise his name, our history, because he – my experience with him – helps me discover, then be, me. Or who I think I am at that time. Our connection sets me on a good path, and we remain lifelong friends.

In fact, Ted marries Dino's sister, Ja, after the death of her first husband, Nick, but that is years from now and a whole other story.

I never knew when to expect Dino's visits. Ted is Tuesdays through Thursdays at 7:00pm. He does not use the window and makes a copy of my building key before he enters through the downstairs front door. Sometime after, we meet his mom, Lilly, and step-dad, Christian, for drinks and a light meal.

Ted thinks abstractly. He says things that get and stay under my skin. For example, he tells me if I had been born male, I would have a huge penis. I ask how he can even know something like that. He says because I have large earlobes and tiny labia. That combination in females means a well-hung male.

This is pure Ted. Senseless but charming, and it sure gets you thinking.

Once I get to know him better, he says he thinks that comes from growing up around people who tell jokes and then explain the punch line. So he moves in the other direction.

He and his family have a long history with this city. Maybe his great grandparents and my great grandmother even knew one another. Ted is perfect (handsome, funny, smart) except not. Dino is steak; Ted is tuna. I know Dino, with his lamb obsession, would not like the steak comparison, but it is how I understand Dino and his solid physicality. And Tuna is fantastic. Just in a different way than steak.

He and Ja are perfect together.

I take Dino's name, Shankus, after I fall in love with him but long before we officially hook up.

I do not tell him.

I do not worry that swiping his name will make him angry; I know that man inside and out. As strong willed as he can be, he wants, at times, others, especially me, to take control. It is the key to our relationship. Me knowing when to take over and when, definitely, not to.

When we meet, as late teenagers, we both have considerable emotional and professional growing to do.

At that time, in the kitchen, I felt small, clumsy, deficient.

Not now.

Now, I realize it had just as much to do with his insecurity as mine because weak people make you feel anxious. They sap confidence. Secure people make you feel strong. I like to think this is true.

Actually it is not. Not a hundred percent true. Some people really believe knocking you off balance is the key to instilling direction, discipline, expertise.

The bullying approach works for some, probably.

I had ballet and piano teachers who did that. I did not respond well. Harshness makes me fumble. Maybe the difference between me, who does not dance or play music, and the other students in those classes, who now dance and play music, is not our talent level but the fact they respond well to iron-fisted instruction. It inspires them to jump higher, land lighter, and memorize routines and musical notes, their tempo and pauses.

I learn best when I am left alone or gently coached.

Maybe that explains why I become a good enough cook to get a scholarship at seventeen. I get my training from books and encouraging friends and relatives.

Being away from home, studying culinary arts at age seventeen, helps me learn who I am. From there, I learn ways I can best navigate our world.

This means identifying a) what my skills are and b) what our world needs.

Then, I match them up.

If I dive unskilled into a need zone, I might do more harm than good.

Employing unnecessary skills is wasteful.

So I have a clear skill set (things culinary) and now just need to identify ways to channel it productively.

When any opportunity not offering that combination comes up, I just say, "No."

Maybe sometimes too harshly.

Example: the afternoon a neighbor, one of the ladies living in a palatial apartment below my garret, knocks on my door, which is ajar, so I don't really have to open it. I just turn from the rice I boil on my cooking plate, see her standing at the entrance, hands clasped, smiling. I hope she has a request for my strong skill set (cooking) to fill a need (hunger, entertainment). I hope she will ask me to whip something up for her and her family, maybe for a party. Instead, she asks if I would mind watching her kids after school. I nearly throw up. Literally. I had just eaten a plate of iffy oysters. I cook rice because a new friend tells me drinking its liquid takes away nausea. I prepare this remedy, hoping to fight off my bad stomach, and when I see her at my entrance, raised eyebrows, big smile, I get my hopes up that her presence is linked to a food preparation request. So I return the smile, ignore my gut – optimism can do that, ease pain, discomfort – and extend my hand. When she says she seeks someone, hopefully me, to mind her children (child care: weak personal skill set), three afternoons a week while she is out of the apartment (child care:

definite need) my response is to withdraw my hand, say, "No." Then, after a moment, she stands there, silent. I say, "No way."

Terrible manners, I know. I speak too soon, too loud, but, in fairness, I am sick and so anxious I might vomit. Where would I do that? No choice but the small sink behind me. Its drain is not very large or functional.

So all this is in play when she asks me not to cook but to mind her children.

I want to explain myself: I am not against her or her children. I have no problem with children I just do not enjoy spending free time with them. I will prepare food for them, even wash up after them, any time. For free. I will cook with them, offering my instruction. For free. But just being around children to watch or play with or supervise them – even getting paid: No.

But I truly feel so sick that I cannot string the sentences together. And that exchange sets up such awkwardness between my neighbor and me. I never get the chance to clear things up. It makes for an uncomfortable living situation the rest of that year.

Being away from home helps me learn who I am, who I can grow into being.

Child minder, no. Chef, yes.

Fashionable, no. Practical, yes.

Big-lunch person, no. Big-dinner person, yes.

Ily McGee, no. Ily Shankus, yes.

But for purely professional reasons.

Polite, no. Rude, yes. (This, though, is learned behavior, not who I am. It is something I am ashamed of and vow to change.)

After several months living away from home, around Christmas time (by now I am eighteen), I am seriously homesick. While swimming laps, I make a decision – as I do so many important ones – that wanting to be someone other than who I am, especially wanting to be these brand new people I see but do not know, even a little bit, is self destructive. I vow to put the brakes on that urge, whatever it takes. That explains my reaction to my neighbor who assumes I want to *watch* her kids in the afternoon. Does she know who I *am*? Anything about *me*?

I remember feeling I wanted to *be* these people here in this new place and feel queasy, ashamed. What a drag, yearning to be someone you don't even know but just pass on the street. What a drag to mistake interest for love. I can be interested in these people, but love? How is that possible? I can feel love for the city, all the simply separate pieces, apart and together, but as far as human beings, no.

Is feeling love for strangers any different than feeling love for movie and rock stars?

What a massive slap in the face to myself, my family, our bees, and our hometown to feel a love and a yearning for difference. You can respect it but love, no. Love takes time, or at least a one-on-one encounter. Not watching people stream by, making things up about them. Making up they have something more to offer than our home, friends, family. That mindset reeks of crumbled self-esteem and a low self-image and is a terrible way to treat people, my people, the ones who work so hard to raise, feed, and teach me. Who rally for my culinary school scholarship. I Love Us! My clothes are *not* wrong; they are mine. Mom picks them out. Beef, corn, and milk are things to love, take pride in. That affection does not negate love for lavender, figs, or fennel. They can all be appreciated together.

I've said how I feel about fashion and now vow that if I ever *do* decide to value appearance I will put in effort to look like my brother Bobby's girlfriend, Val. She, a long distance runner, has long blond hair – to her waist, slightly wavy, Genevieve-like (or how I imagine Genevieve's hair to be). Val is in heavy eye make up (even on her runs) but light lip-gloss. She wears really tight clothes, so you can see her beautiful figure even in winter when she wears thick jackets. She drinks diet pop with ice and chews gum and wears tons of jewelry (not the expensive kind) and always gets her nails done (even when she is older and runs a sustainable farm). What I am saying is that Val goes all out with her fashion in a way that respects her roots, and if I were ever to care about fashion, I would follow her lead (we have similar roots) rather than the restrained kind of elegance I see on these streets, which has nothing to do with *my* roots, though maybe my valiant Great Grandma's, but that is far down the line, really. You know?

Incidentally, when my culinary school friends (including Ted) visit me, they describe their iconic city as tired, drab, and worn out and find things in my town and state to love. Farms, bees, jams. We jog down vacant roads, swim in the lake, make campfires. They tell me how romantic the scenery is, how handsome Dad is, how they want to dress like Mom, how they love our foods.

Shankus vs. McGee

I am proud of our family name, McGee. I am proud of our Irish heritage, of the orange, white, and green, but decide to change it for professional reasons. Why?

Fucking Izzie McGee.

The mega millionaire (maybe billionaire) who is born, raised, and living in our state. This guy does bad thing after bad thing but always slips out of solid convictions. He pollutes streams, rivers, lakes, air. He runs injurious, high-risk work sites and discriminates, harasses. He is frequently sued, but nothing ever sticks. He is that of kind nasty.

He is no relation.

I was going to say how he single-handedly wreaks damage, but that, of course, is The Myth. That rotten men like Izzie are solo cowboys who commit crimes and weasel out of punishment, all alone. That never happens. Guys like him have massive, loyal support systems that include plenty of powerful, *respected* people in high places.

He is no relation.

But you must see how hard it is for me to separate my name, Ily McGee, from his?

It is easy to fly under the radar when you are microscopic, but I plan to grow into a recognizable brand, which means meeting with potential backers and seeking out customers. PR for a new business is everything. Ily McGee suggests Izzie McGee, plain and simple. Always will.

Izzie is a Bad Guy. Seriously.

And my family already has to deal with everyone asking us constantly if we are related to Izzie, and not one of us is even well known. Yet. Like I will soon be.

Ily McGee signifies. Ily Shankus, in contrast, carries no baggage. No one has that name, at least in the chef world. Yet. It would be a good name choice, even if there were no Dino.

But, lucky for me, there is Dino because I would not be the chef I am, the chef I will continue develop into being, without him.

Ted (as I said, we stay friends) advises me not to change names. Says, instead, I should show courage, stick up for my family and, in fact, for all McGees everywhere. Says I should shift the significance of McGee by becoming more famous and powerful than Izzie. By blowing him out of the park, county, state. That an Ily McGee success will make people forget Izzie, blot out that there even is an Izzie. McGee will move out of the realm of deplorable into the realm of admirable. Ted is utopian. I tell him so.

"Okay," he says, "How about this: Rather than battle Izzie with an Ily rise to the top, how about employing legal and illegal tactics to fight the bastard, to identify charges that stick, that will expose him as the dangerous criminal he is?"

We have several late evenings discussing ways to achieve this. I can use my name to access secret information about him, perhaps posing as his niece, daughter, or even wife. I could become a detective, spy. Channel Great Grandma. Ted would help me. Once we lay the groundwork, we could call in the cops, the F.B.I. What these conversations do for me is make me wonder what it would be like to have choices, to head down an unfamiliar path and see where it leads. I cannot. I am a cook. Plain and simple. There is no other choice for me. If I cook in a diner or a kitchen or open my own restaurant is less important than the fact I Must Cook. I am born this way.

But my brother and his now wife Val, are not. They, and others, including Ted, go on to take on this cause with eventual great success. They bust Mr. Dick-less. I play my part in this, too. (Izzie is a foodie.) This is a good and inspiring story but for another time.

By the way, when I say Dick-less, I do not mean the condition is negative, being built that way myself. I use it because it is a term that I happen to know would particularly bother Izzie.

I knew Dino and I would wind up together. I just did not know when.

Patience is sexy. The name change – McGee to Shankus – comes several years after culinary school when I return home, attend community college, and explore publishing, local TV appearances, and future restaurant ownership. I understand using the name Shankus can be perceived as robbing, but I never steal a thing in my life, not even a recipe. In fact, every time I serve the beef-heart chili Dino and I develop together in cooking school, I credit him and me. ("Ily" and "Dino" is on the menu.) It gives me an idea for a cookbook ("Dino and Ily" – it sounds better with the consonant first) and gives me the excuse to work with him after all these years. Pitching the cookbook idea. Organ meats but strictly with grass-fed animals. From Bobby and Val's sustainable farm.

The cookbook's title: *D&I: Offal*

The book does very well, and, as anyone with business sense knows, it is not just because of the recipes. It is because of certain marketing strategies including the title: catchy, unusual, appealing. And of course there is the sway of our investors.

There is a reason for the abbreviations.

I have a long-term goal beyond the cookbook. I want to co-own a restaurant with Dino named "Dino & Ily." I do not want to blow this venture by giving it the same name as our first book. Suppose it fails? *D&I: Offal* keeps the door open in ways *Dino & Ily: Offal* would not.

It would be completely disrespectful even to consider using the name "Shankus" for the cookbook. His parents might one day want to write a cookbook – or perhaps have a TV show. If they do. they should have at least the choice to name it Shankus.

Ily Shankus. There is no chef with a name even close to it.

– END of Vol 1 –

SONGS

"Autosuggestion"
Ian Kevin Curtis, Peter Hook,
Stephen Paul David Morris
and Bernard Sumner

"Just Fine"
ADLER, CISCO / DUTTON,
GARRETT

"Must I Paint You A Picture"
Billy Bragg

"People"
Jule Styne, Bob Merrill

"Sitting"
Cat Stevens

"Tender"
Damon Alban, Graham Coxon

"Up on Cripple Creek"
Robbie Robertson

"We are Family"
Nile Rodgers, Bernard
Edwards

BOOKS QUOTED

Bible Ecclesiastes 10:18

*The Making of Americans:
Being a History of a Family's
Progress*, Gertrude Stein,
Contact Press, Paris, 1925.

Leaves of Grass, Walt Whitman.
Self/Fulton St. Printing Shop.
Brooklyn, 1855.

Anna Karenina, Leo Tolstoy.
The Russian Messenger,
Moscow, 1878.

MENTIONED

Anias Nin quote (Google;
no cited source)

*The Sadeian Woman: And
the Ideology of Pornography*,
Angela Carter. Pantheon,
London, 1978.

Woodstock (film) Michael
Wadleigh Director, 1970.

Lynn Crawford is a novelist and arts writer living and working in Detroit. Her books include *Solow, Blow, Fortification Resort* (a selection of art related sestinas) and the novels *Simply Separate People* and *Simple Separate People, Two.* She is a Kresge Literary Arts Fellow and a 2016 Rauschenberg Writing Fellow.